W9-AFT-614

Probability
and
Chi-Square
for Biology Students

SANDRA F. COOPER

THOMAS R. MERTENS

BRIAR CLIFF COLLEGE
LIBRARY
SIOUX CITY, IOWA

EMI EDUCATIONAL METHODS, INC./CHICAGO

We are indebted to the Literary Executor of the late Sir Ronald A. Fisher, F.R.S., Cambridge, to Dr. Frank Yates, F.R.S., Rothamsted, and to Messrs. Oliver and Boyd Ltd., Edinburgh, for permission to reprint Table III from their book *Statistical Tables for Biological, Agricultural and Medical Research.*

Library of Congress Catalog Card Number 77-79901

Copyright 1969 by Sandra F. Cooper
and Thomas R. Mertens

First Published 1969 by
EDUCATIONAL METHODS, INC.
20 East Huron Street Chicago, Illinois 60611

All Rights Reserved
Printed in U.S.A.

9 8 7 6 5 4 3 2 1

QH
324
.C6x

Contents

TO THE STUDENT

HOW TO USE THIS BOOK

68682

To The Student

Basic to understanding a number of scientific disciplines is an appreciation of fundamental concepts of probability. Various biological disciplines (e.g., genetics and ecology) make use of these concepts and of simple statistical tests such as the chi-square test. For example, probability considerations are essential to the basic laws of heredity developed by Gregor Mendel and by the classical transmission geneticists of the early twentieth century. Furthermore, the chi-square test is a tool used in analyzing the data obtained in genetics crosses and in other types of biological investigations. You will not progress very far in the study of biology before you encounter the need for the basic concepts of probability and chi-square.

Many science students, and perhaps most biology students, encounter some need for formal instruction in these basic principles. This book has been designed to assist you in obtaining such instruction. It has been written in an inductive fashion, leading you from specific examples and facts to broad principles and generalizations. The authors have purposely *not* given you "rules" to follow, but they have provided you with meaningful examples that should enable you to conclude what rules apply to the various situations discussed. This approach should insure that generalizations, once made, are meaningful to you.

Probability and Chi-Square is different from most books you have read. It is a programed text. It consists of appropriate background information followed by a series of questions and problems which you are to answer. The answers to these questions and problems are also provided, and great care has been taken to outline the reasoning process underlying the answers given.

You will find this book most helpful if you are just beginning to learn about probability and chi-square. On the other hand, if you are experienced in these matters, you will find that the book will provide you with a suitable summary and review of familiar material. The more knowledgeable student will find the content of the book sufficiently sophistocated to be challenging, while the beginning student will find it well enough structured to lead him, step-by-step, to an understanding of some important concepts.

A knowledge of basic Mendelian genetics and of elementary algebra will be helpful to you when studying this program. If you need review, we suggest you consult appropriate high school or college textbooks dealing with these topics before you get too far along with your study of this program.

Because of the organization of this program, you must progress through it from the beginning to the end. You cannot skip around and retain the meaningful structure of the book. Rather, you should progress through the program at the speed necessary for you. Parts of the book may be more readily comprehended than others; you should vary your study speed to fit the level of difficulty of the material with which you are dealing. Progress quizzes at appropriate places in the program will enable you to test your comprehension of the material you have been studying. The end result of conscientious study of this book will enable you to do the following things:

- Determine the number of *possible* ways in which a series of separate events can occur.
- Determine the *probability* that one particular event among several possibilities will occur.
- Determine the probability of the occurrence of two or more *simultaneously* occurring *independent* events.
- Determine the probability of the occurrence of *either* one *or* the other of two or more separate events.
- Expand the binomial $(a + b)^N$ and use the expanded binomial in calculating probabilities.
- *Calculate* and *interpret* chi-square in determining the goodness-of-fit of data to a particular hypothesized ratio.

How To Use This Book

This may be a new type of instructional book for many of you. Its subject matter has been broken down into a series of numbered frames. The subject matter has been organized or programmed in such a way that the book will serve as a self-instructional program. Using this book you can teach yourself the fundamentals of probability and chi-square. Each frame in the program builds on information you have learned in preceding frames. For that reason it is important that you do not skip around in the program. The sequence of the frames is important and is designed to help you learn more efficiently.

Respond at Every Frame

Some frames present new information; others review material presented earlier; many of the frames consist of problems to be solved using the information developed in preceding frames. Every frame presents a learning situation requiring you to respond. You may be asked to make one of the following types of responses:
- writing an answer in a blank space;
- answering a question in one or two words;
- writing a sentence, phrase, or clause in answer to a question;
- choosing the correct answer from several alternatives;
- solving a problem.

It is important that you both write your answers and make the calculations necessary to solve the problems. Once you have written your answer, you will want to find out whether you have responded correctly. Programed instruction provides you with immediate feedback by giving you the answers to the questions asked. The answers are separated from the question by a single line. The immediate feedback is an important part of the learning process and will enable you to readily determine how your learning is progressing. *Do not look at the correct answer until after you have made the necessary calculations and recorded your own answer.* If you look before answering you will only impair your own learning.

Use an Answer Mask

To avoid seeing the correct answer inadvertently before recording your own answer, make an Answer Mask by folding an 8½" x 11" piece of paper in half.

1. Now, as you start each new page, cover the page with the Answer Mask.
2. Move the mask down until you expose a heavy horizontal line that runs across the entire page. This line separates each frame from its correct answer.
3. When you reach the horizontal line, stop moving the mask. Read the frame carefully and record your answer. Make sure you *write* each answer; in those problems involving calculations show the steps you used in reaching the answer. Do *not* simply "think" the answer and then go on. Considerably more learning will be accomplished by actually writing your answer.
4. Now slide the mask down to reveal the correct answer. If the frame which you are studying contains several parts [(a), (b), (c), etc.], you may reveal the answer to each part before proceeding to the next part of the frame.
5. If your answer was correct, move the mask down to the next heavy horizontal line and proceed with the new frame you have just uncovered.
6. If your answer was wrong, go back, re-study the frame (and if necessary re-study several preceding frames) until you understand your error and know why the answer given is correct. Then proceed to the next frame. (Note that in the answers to the frames, care has been taken to show the reasoning processes you must employ in arriving at the correct answer.)

Progress Quizzes and Comprehensive Review

Four progress quizzes are included at appropriate places in this book. Each quiz will help you and your instructor to evaluate how well you have mastered the material just covered. Answers to the quizzes are provided only in the Teacher's Manual.

The comprehensive review at the end of the book serves as a summary of the entire program. Problems representative of each of the major parts of the book are included in this review. You *must* be able to solve the problems in the review if you are successfully to complete the final examination.

Basic Probability Principles

Section 1: Possibility

1. Our first concern in preparing to deal with probabilities is to determine all of the possibilities, or alternative ways in which an event can happen. In tossing a coin, for example, there are two possibilities, heads or tails. For a six-sided die there are six possibilities or alternatives, since any one of the six sides may be turned face up. From a 52-card deck of cards, how many alternatives are there? In other words, any one of how many possible cards may be drawn?_____

52; If you draw only one card it could be any one of the 52 cards in the deck.

2. A coin is flipped into the air. It can land either heads or tails. There are how many possibilities?_____

2

3. Two coins are flipped into the air simultaneously.
   (a) Coin 1 has how many possibilities?_____
   (b) Coin 2 has how many possibilities?_____
   (c) For the two coins *together,* there are how many possibilities?
   _____

(a) Coin 1 has 2 possibilities—heads (H) or tails (T).
(b) Coin 2 has 2 possibilities—(H) or (T).
(c) Coins 1 *and* 2 together have 4 possibilities *i.e.,*
   $2 \times 2 = 4$ possibilities.

4. Two coins are flipped into the air simultaneously. What are the four possible combinations for the 2 coins?

Possibilities for Coin 1

	H	T
H	HH	
T		

Possibilities For Coin 2

Write H or T in the chart at left to obtain the 4 different combinations.

Possibilities For Coin 1

Possibilities For Coin 2

Note in the checkerboard that there can be HT or TH. Therefore, there are two possible ways of getting a head *and a* tail. It might be argued by some that there are only 3 possibilities for both coins (*i.e.,* two heads, two tails, or a head and a tail), HT and TH each being "a head and a tail." However, if we designate the order, such as H_1T_2 (heads for Coin 1, tails for Coin 2) then we have four different possibilities *i.e.,* $2 \times 2 = 4$.

5. A boy and a girl, both students in biology, take an examination. Each of them can get either a passing or a failing grade on the examination.
    (a) How many possibilities are there with respect to passing or failing for each student taking the examination?_____
    (b) How many possible combinations of passing or failing grades are there for the boy *and* girl together?_____

(a) There are 2 possibilities for each student, Pass or Fail.
(b)

Boy		Girl		Possible Grade Combinations For Boy And Girl
2	$\times$	2	$=$	4

6. A boy and a girl take an examination. Each can either pass or fail the examination. Considering the two students at the same time, there are 4 possible combinations of grades for them. What are these combinations? Fill in the chart including the headings.

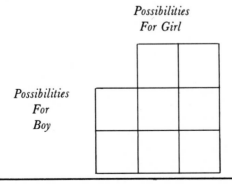

Possibilities For Girl

Possibilities For Boy

Possibilities
For Girl

	P	F
P	PP	PF
F	FP	FF

Possibilities For Boy (label to the left of the table)

7. Suppose letter grades are given on the next biology examination. Each of the two students can score an A, B, C, D, or F.

(a) How many possible grades can the boy earn?_____

(b) How many possible grades can the girl earn?_____

(c) How many possible grade combinations are there for the boy and the girl?_____

(d) Show all the possible grade combinations for the boy and the girl.

Possibilities For Girl

	A	B	C	D	F
A					
B					
C					
D					
F					

Possibilities For Boy (label to the left of the table)

(a) The boy can earn 5 possible grades: A, B, C, D, or F.
(b) The girl can also earn 5 possible grades: A, B, C, D, or F.
(c) For the boy *and* girl there are 5 x 5 = 25 possible combinations.
(d) The possible grade combinations for the boy and the girl are:

Possibilities For Girl

		A	B	C	D	F
	A	AA	AB	AC	AD	AF
	B	BA	BB	BC	BD	BF
Possibilities *For Boy*	C	CA	CB	CC	CD	CF
	D	DA	DB	DC	DD	DF
	F	FA	FB	FC	FD	FF

8. A pair of dice is rolled. One die is white, the other red. Each die has six faces.
    (a) How many possibilities are there for the white die? _____
    (b) For the red die? _____
    (c) How many possible combinations are there for the red die and white die together? _____

(a) There are 6 possibilities for the white die.
(b) There are 6 possibilities for the red die.
(c) There are 36 possibilities for the red die and white die together.

White		*Red*		*Possible Combinations*
6	X	6	=	36

9. A deck of playing cards consists of four suits: Hearts, Clubs, Spades, and Diamonds. Each suit contains 13 cards, 2 through 10 plus a Jack, a Queen, a King, and an Ace.

    (a) If any one card is drawn from the 52-card deck, how many possibilities are there? _____

    (b) If a Heart is drawn from a 52-card deck, how many possibilities are there? _____

    (c) If a five is drawn from a 52-card deck, how many possibilities are there? _____

(a) 52; (b) 13; (c) 4

10. Two cards are drawn from a deck of 52 cards. The first card is a five, the other is a seven. The first card, a five, could belong to any one of the four suits. The second card, a seven, could belong to any one of the four suits. Therefore, there are how many possible combinations of suits for the two cards? _____

The first card can be a five from any of the 4 suits: Hearts, Clubs, Spades, or Diamonds. Therefore, there are four possibilities for the first card. The same is true of the second card. Therefore,

Card I		Card II		Possible Combinations
4	$\times$	4	$=$	16

11. In beans two pairs of genes are concerned with two different seed characteristics. The phenotype or appearance of the bean is controlled by these genes. One gene pair controls whether the seed has smooth or wrinkled texture. The other gene pair controls whether the seed is circular or oval in shape.

    (a) How many different phenotypes are there concerning seed texture? _____

    (b) Seed shape? _____

(c) How many possible combinations of these two characteristics are there?_____

(d) What are the various phenotypic combinations?_____

Seed Texture

Seed Shape

(a) There are two possibilities concerning seed texture—smooth or wrinkled.

(b) There are two possibilities concerning seed shape—circular or oval.

(c) The number of possible phenotypic combinations equals 4.

Seed Texture		*Seed Shape*	
2	$\times$	2	$= 4$

(d) The possible phenotypic combinations are:

Seed Texture

Seed Shape		smooth	wrinkled
	oval	oval smooth	oval wrinkled
	circular	circular smooth	circular wrinkled

12. In living organisms there are 20 different commonly occurring amino acids. A dipeptide is made up of 2 amino acids.

    (a) There are how many possible amino acids for the first amino acid in a dipeptide? _____

    (b) There are how many possible amino acids for the second amino acid in a dipeptide? _____

    (c) There are how many possible dipeptides? _____

(a) For the first amino acid in the dipeptide there are 20 possible amino acids.

(b) There are also 20 possibilities for the second amino acid in the dipeptide.

(c) Therefore, there are $20 \times 20 = 400$ different dipeptides possible.

First Amino Acid		Second Amino Acid		Dipeptides
20	$\times$	20	$=$	400

13. A student was given an unknown dipeptide. In the laboratory he eliminated, for the first amino acid, 15 of the 20 possible amino acids; for the second amino acid, he eliminated all except three. How many combinations of amino acids are possible for his unknown dipeptide? _____

First Amino Acid		Second Amino Acid		Possible Dipeptides
5	$\times$	3	$=$	15

14. We are now prepared to formulate a generalization or a principle. *If one event can happen in "a" number of ways and a second event, occurring simultaneously and being independent of the first event, can happen in "b" number of ways, then the two events together can occur in "a" times "b" number of ways or the product of the possibilities for each separate event.*

8

In other words, when two events occur, the number of possibilities for both occurring together is: (circle one letter)
  (a) the number of possibilities for the first event added to the number of possibilities for the second event.
  (b) the number of possibilities of the first event multiplied by the number of possibilities for the second event.
For this to occur, the two events must be: (circle one letter)
  (c) dependent on each other.
  (d) independent of each other.

(b) the number of possibilities for the first event multiplied by the number of possibilities for the second event.
(d) independent of each other.

15. Our principle can be extended to determine the number of possibilities for 3 or more independently occurring events.
There are 3 students who take an examination and each student can pass or fail.
  (a) With respect to passing or failing, how many possibilities are there for each student?_____
  (b) How many possibilities are there for all 3 students?_____
  (c) List all the possible combinations for the 3 students.

(a) There are 2 possibilities for each student—passing or failing.
(b) For all 3 students, there are:

Student 1		Student 2		Student 3		All 3
2	×	2	×	2	=	2^3 or 8

(c) The possible combinations for the 3 students are:
  1. P P P   5. F F P
  2. P P F   6. F P F
  3. P F P   7. P F F
  4. F P P   8. F F F

16. Tripeptides are made of <u>three</u> amino acids. Remembering that there are 20 different amino acids which commonly occur, how many different possible tripeptides are there?_____

Amino Acid I		Amino Acid II		Amino Acid III	Possible Tripeptides
20	×	20	×	20	= 20^3 or 8000

17. How many different tripeptides are possible if we know that the middle amino acid in the tripeptide is alanine?_____

Amino Acid I		Amino Acid II		Amino Acid III	Possible Tripeptides
20	×	1	×	20	= 400

18. In a family of three children,
    (a) how many possibilities are there for the sex of the first child?_____
    (b) how many possibilities are there for the sex of the second child?_____
    (c) the third child?_____

(a) For the first child, there are 2 possibilities—a boy or a girl.
(b) 2—a boy or a girl.
(c) 2—a boy or a girl.

19. In a family of three children,
    (a) how many different combinations of boys and girls are possible?_____

(b) List these possible combinations.

(a) *Child 1*   *Child 2*   *Child 3*   *Family*

$\quad\;\; 2 \quad\times\quad 2 \quad\times\quad 2 \quad = \quad 2^3 \text{ or } 8$

(b) The different combinations of boys and girls in a family of 3 children are:

1. B B B   5. G G B
2. B B G   6. G B G
3. B G B   7. B G G
4. G B B   8. G G G

20. There are four nitrogen-containing bases found in the deoxyribonucleic acid (DNA) molecule. These are adenine, guanine, cytosine, and thymine.

(a) For a four-base sequence, such as GCTA, CAGG, or AAAA, etc., how many possible combinations are there?_____

(b) For a three-base sequence, such as CTG, TTT, or ACG, etc., how many possible combinations are there?_____

(a) *First Base* *Second base* *Third Base* *Fourth Base* *4-Base Sequence*

$\quad\; 4 \quad\times\quad 4 \quad\times\quad 4 \quad\times\quad 4 \quad = 4^4 \text{ or } 256$

(b) *First Base*   *Second Base*   *Third Base*   *3-Base Sequence*

$\quad\; 4 \quad\times\quad 4 \quad\times\quad 4 \quad = 4^3 \text{ or } 64$

21. A female has the genotype *AaBb*.

(a) How many different kinds of gametes can she produce?_____

(b) What are they?_____

(a) *Trait A*   *Trait B*   *Gametic Possibilities*
   2 possibilities   X   2 possibilities   =   4
   (*A* and *a*)   (*B* and *b*)

(b) Female Gametic Possibilities: *AB, Ab, aB, ab.*

22. A male has the genotype *AABb*.
   (a) How many different kinds of gametes can he produce?_____
   (b) What are they?_____

(a) *Trait A*   *Trait B*   *Gametic*
                                            Possibilities
   1 possibility   X   2 possibilities   =   2
     (*A*)   (*B* and *b*)

(b) Male Gametic Possibilities: *AB, Ab.*

23. A female has the genotype *AaBb* and a male has the genotype *AABb*.
   (a) How many possible combinations of male and female gametes are there?_____
   (b) Show these possibilities in a "checkerboard" or chart. In genetics, this "checkerboard" diagram is called a Punnett Square.

(a) *Female Gametic*   *Male Gametic*   *Gametic Combinations*
    Possibilities   *Possibilities*
        4   ×   2   =   8

(b) The 8 possibilities may be illustrated as follows:

Female Gametic Possibilities

	AB	*Ab*	*aB*	*ab*
Male Gametic *Possibilities* *AB*	*AABB*	*AABb*	*AaBB*	*AaBb*
Ab	*AAbB*	*AAbb*	*AabB*	*Aabb*

Note that just as with Heads and Tails, not all of the 8 possible combinations are different.

24. The total number of possibilities resulting from any number of independently occurring events is determined by: (circle one letter)
  (a) adding the number of possibilities for each respective event.
  (b) multiplying the number of possibilities for each respective event.

(b) multiplying

Section 2: Probability of Simultaneous Events—Multiply

25. *Probability* is the chance that one particular event will happen out of all the possibilities. Probability may be expressed as a fraction, a percentage, or a ratio. In this text, we will usually express probability as a fraction.

If a coin is flipped,
  (a) In how many different ways can it land? _____
  (b) What chance do you have of getting a head?_____
  (c) A tail? _____

(a) A coin can land in two different ways, heads or tails.
(b) The probability of a head: 1 chance out of 2 possibilities or ½.
(c) The probability of a tail: 1 chance out of 2 possibilities or ½.

26. A deck of cards contains four aces. If you hold only these four aces in your hand, what is the probability of someone drawing the ace of diamonds from your hand?_____

One chance out of four possibilities or ¼.

27. From the entire deck of cards, the probability of drawing an ace the first time is _____.

Four chances out of 52 = 4/52 or 1/13.

28. The probability of rolling a die and getting a three is_____.

---

1 chance out of 6 = 1/6.

29. Two dice are rolled simultaneously.
    (a) The probability of getting a "3" on the first die is _____ .
    (b) The probability of getting a "5" on the second die is _____ .
    (c) The probability of getting a "3" and a "5" in that order
        is _____ .

(a) The probability of getting a "3" on the first die is 1/6.
(b) The probability of getting a "5" on the second die is 1/6.
(c) Therefore, the probability of getting a "3" and a "5' in that order is 1/6 x 1/6 = 1/36.

30. The probability of drawing the five of hearts from one deck of cards and, simultaneously, the ace of spades from a second deck would be _____ .

One chance out of 52 for each draw; therefore,

First Draw		Second Draw		Both
1/52	×	1/52	=	1/2704

31. The probability of getting a base sequence of GATT in a nucleotide chain of four nucleotides would be _____ .

The probability of getting guanine for base number one is 1 out of 4 possible bases, or 1/4, and the probability of getting adenine for base number two is 1 chance out of 4 possible bases or 1/4, etc. Therefore, the probability for the particular base sequence GATT is 1/4 x 1/4 x 1/4 x 1/4 = 1/256.

Base 1		Base 2		Base 3		Base 4		4-Base Sequence
1/4	x	1/4	x	1/4	x	1/4	=	1/256

32. In a family of 2 children,
    (a) what is the probability that both will be boys?_____
    (b) both girls?_____

(a) The probability is ½ that each child will be a boy and ½ that each child will be a girl. Therefore,

	Child 1		Child 2	Both
Boys	½	×	½	=¼ that both are boys
(b) Girls	½	×	½	=¼ that both are girls

33. What is the probability that a couple would have 2 boys and 2 girls in that order?_____

There are 2 possibilities in each case, i.e., for Child 1 there are two possibilities, a boy or a girl; for Child 2 there are 2 possibilities, a boy or a girl, etc. Therefore, for Child 1, the probability of having a boy is 1 out of 2 possibilities or ½. For Child 2, the probability of having a boy is also 1 out of 2 possibilities or ½. For Child 3, the probability of having a girl is 1 chance out of 2 or ½, and this is also true for Child 4. Following this, the probability of 2 boys followed by 2 girls is

Child 1		Child 2		Child 3		Child 4		Four Children
1/2	x	1/2	x	1/2	x	1/2	=	1/16

34. In a family of 4 children consisting of 2 boys (B) and 2 girls (G), there are 6 different combinations or orders possible. These are:

1. B G B G	4. G B G B
2. G G B B	5. B G G B
3. B B G G	6. G B B G

What is the probability that a couple would have 2 boys and 2 girls in *any one* of the six possible combinations?_____

The probability for any *one* of these different orders is:

The Prob. of	Child 1		Child 2		Child 3		Child 4		Four Children
BGBG	½	x	½	x	½	x	½	=	1/16
GGBB	½	x	½	x	½	x	½	=	1/16
BBGG	½	x	½	x	½	x	½	=	1/16
GBGB	½	x	½	x	½	x	½	=	1/16
BGGB	½	x	½	x	½	x	½	=	1/16
GBBG	½	x	½	x	½	x	½	=	1/16

Note that the probability of any one of the six possible combinations is 1/16.

35. A box contains 25 blue marbles, 20 yellow marbles, 15 green marbles, and 40 red marbles.
 (a) What is the probability of picking, blindfolded, a yellow marble?_____
 (b) A blue marble? _____
 (c) A green marble?_____

(a) The probability of getting a yellow marble would be 20 out of 100 (since there are 100 marbles in the container) = 20/100 or 1/5.
(b) Probability of a blue marble = 25/100 or 1/4.
(c) Probability of a green marble = 15/100 or 3/20.

36. An experiment was conducted in an attempt to determine the ability of insects to perceive and distinguish between colors. Bees were used as the experimental insects. Disks of yellow and blue were placed on bee hives and the bees were observed to "choose" one disk or the other. Bees of three different strains were used. The following observations were made:

Selection Preference of Bees of Strain 1		Selection Preference of Bees of Strain 2		Selection Preference of Bees of Strain 3	
Yellow	Blue	Yellow	Blue	Yellow	Blue
4/5	1/5	2/3	1/3	1/2	1/2

The bee from Strain 1 was observed to "choose" the yellow disk 4/5 of the time, the bee of Strain 2 "chose" the yellow disk 2/3 of the time, and the bee from Strain 3, 1/2 of the time. Assuming the "choices" to be independent of each other,

(a) What is the probability of bees of Strains 1, 2, and 3 all "choosing" yellow?_____
(b) Of Strains 1 and 2 "choosing" yellow and Strain 3 "choosing" blue, (i.e., YYB)?_____
(c) The probability of BBY?_____
(d) Of BBB?_____

	Strain 1		Strain 2		Strain 3	
(a)	4/5	×	2/3	×	1/2	= 8/30 or 4/15
(b)	4/5	×	2/3	×	1/2	= 8/30 or 4/15
(c)	1/5	×	1/3	×	1/2	= 1/30
(d)	1/5	×	1/3	×	1/2	= 1/30

37. The gene for albinism (a) is recessive to the gene for normal pigmentation (A) in human beings. If two individuals, both of whom are heterozygous (i.e., Aa) for the albino characteristics, are mated:

(a) How many kinds of gametes can each parent produce?_____
(b) How many possible combinations of these gametes are there?_____
(c) What are these possible combinations?

Female

Male

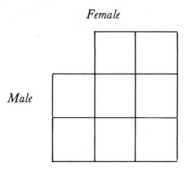

(d) What is the probability of an albino being born to parents both of whom are heterozygous for the albino characteristic?_____

(a) Since the parents are both heterozygous, their gametes can contain either gene *A* (normal) or gene *a* (albinism). Therefore, each parent produces 2 types of gametes concerning albinism—*A* and *a*.

(b) The number of possible combinations of these are:

Male Gametes		Female Gametes		Zygotic Combinations
2	×	2	=	4

(c) There are 4 combinations as follows:

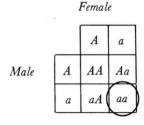

Female

	A	*a*
Male *A*	*AA*	*Aa*
a	*aA*	*aa*

(d) Therefore, the probability of an albino being born to parents heterozygous for this trait is 1 out of 4 or ¼.

38. Two individuals are heterozygous for the albino characteristic.
    (a) What is the probability of their having an albino child?_____
    (b) What is the probability of their having a boy?_____
    (c) What is the probability of their having an albino boy?_____

(a) Probability of an albino is ¼.
(b) Probability of a boy is ½.
(c)

Probability of An Albino		Probability of A Boy		Probability of An Albino Boy
1/4	×	1/2	=	1/8

39. Two individuals are heterozygous for the albino characteristic.
   (a) What is the probability of their having four consecutive albinos?_____
   (b) What is the probability of their having a boy?_____
   (c) A girl?_____
   (d) What is the probability of their having four consecutive albinos, the first a boy, followed by 3 girls?_____

(a)

Prob. of First Albino		Prob. of Second Albino		Prob. of Third Albino		Prob. of Fourth Albino		Prob. of 4 Consec. Albinos
1/4	x	1/4	x	1/4	x	1/4	=	1/256

(b) The probability of having a boy is 1/2.

(c) Likewise, the probability of a girl is 1/2.

(d)

Probability of 4 Consec. Albinos		Prob. of a Boy		Prob. of a Girl		Prob. of a Girl		Prob. of a Girl		Probability of 4 Consec. Albinos, First a Boy and then 3 Girls
1/256	x	1/2	x	1/2	x	1/2	x	1/2	=	1/4096

Or this could be worked out a second way:

Probability of First Child Being Albino		Probability of First Child Being a Boy		Probability of An Albino Boy
1/4	×	1/2	=	1/8
Second Child Being Albino		Second Child Being a Girl		An Albino Girl
1/4	×	1/2	=	1/8
Third Child Being Albino		Third Child Being a Girl		An Albino Girl
1/4	×	1/2	=	1/8
Fourth Child Being Albino		Fourth Child Being a Girl		An Albino Girl
1/4	×	1/2	=	1/8

$$1/8 \times 1/8 \times 1/8 \times 1/8 = 1/4096$$

40. Remembering that the probability of heterozygous parents having an albino is ¼:
    (a) What is the probability of their having a normal child?_____
    (b) Four consecutive normal children?_____

(a) Three of the four possible types of offspring would be normal (*AA, Aa, aA*). Therefore, the probability of heterozygous parents having a child with the normal pigmentation is 3 chances out of 4 or ¾.
(b) 3/4 x 3/4 x 3/4 x 3/4 = 81/256

41. Briefly, in blood type inheritance, the gene for type *O* may be considered a recessive; the genes for *A* and *B* as dominant to gene *O*, but co-dominant with respect to each other. If an individual receives the gene for type *O* blood from one parent and the gene for type *B* blood from the other parent, the individual will have:
    (a) What blood type?_____
    (b) If an individual receives the gene for type *O* blood from one parent and the gene for type *A* blood from the other parent, the individual will have what blood type?_____
    (c) If each parent contributes a gene for type *O* blood to their offspring, this offspring will have what blood type?_____
    (d) If one parent contributes a gene for type *A* blood and the offspring has type AB blood, the second parent contributed a gene for what blood type?_____

(a) Type B—because the gene for type *B* dominates the gene for type *O* blood.
(b) Type A—because the gene for type *A* dominates the gene for type *O* blood.
(c) Type O—the genotype is *OO*, therefore, the recessive genes are expressed.
(d) *B*—because both genes, *A* and *B,* are present in the type AB offspring and each is expressed equally i.e., *A* and *B* are co-dominant with respect to each other.

42. An heterozygous male having blood type A (*i.e.*, having geno-type *AO*), marries a female having type AB blood.
   (a) What are the possible blood types for their children?_____
   (b) What is the probability of their having children with type A blood?_____

(a)   *Male Genotype*   *Female Genotype*

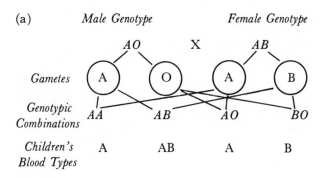

(b) There are 2 chances out of 4 for blood type A, therefore, $2/4$ or $1/2$.

43.

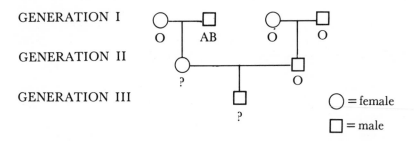

In the human pedigree diagramed above, the blood type is shown under each individual where it is known.

(a) What is the probability of the female in the second generation having type A blood?_____
(b) Type B blood?_____
(c) What is the probability of the male in the third generation having type A blood?_____
(d) Type B blood?_____
(e) Type AB blood?_____
(f) Type O blood?_____.

(a) As we look at the pedigree, we see there are two possible genotypes for the second generation female: AO or BO. Therefore, the probability that she will have type A blood is $\frac{1}{2}$.

(b) Likewise, the probability of her having type B blood is also $\frac{1}{2}$.

(c) For the third generation male, there are three possibilities, depending on the blood type of his mother. She can be type A or type B, but in each case her genotype carries the recessive O gene (since her mother was blood type O). Therefore, she can contribute an A or O gene or a B or an O gene to her son. Therefore, the probability of the second generation female having the gene for type A $= \frac{1}{2}$. The probability that if she is type A that she will transmit the A gene $= \frac{1}{2}$. $\frac{1}{2}$ x $\frac{1}{2} = \frac{1}{4} =$ probability of the third generation male being type A. Since the second generation male has type O blood, he can transmit only the gene for type O blood. Therefore, the probability of the third generation male having type A blood depends entirely upon the gene transmitted to him by his mother.

(d) Probability of the third generation male being type B $= \frac{1}{4}$ (see explanation for part (c).

(e) Probability of the third generation male having type AB blood $= 0/4$; no chance, because his father has type O blood and must contribute one O gene to his son's genotype.

(f) The probability of type O blood for the third generation male equals $\frac{1}{2}$. The probability that his mother passes on the O gene is $\frac{1}{2}$, whether she is A or B type. The father is certain to pass on the O gene; therefore, $\frac{1}{2}$ x $1 = \frac{1}{2}$.

23

44. As a result of Mendel's work with garden peas, he proposed what are now recognized as the basic principles of genetics, one of which is as follows: the "hereditary factors" (now called genes) are segregated independently of each other into the gametes.

Garden peas have seven pairs of chromosomes. Mendel was fortunate indeed, to have selected for his work seven different traits, each of which was carried on a different one of the seven chromosome pairs. What would be the probability of selecting seven traits at random in the garden pea, each trait being carried on a different one of the seven chromosome pairs?_____

About 1/163 (See next two frames for explanation.)

45. In order to see how the answer was obtained in the frame above, proceed as follows:

The first gene can be on any chromosome pair of the seven. Therefore, the probability of the allele for the first trait being on one of the seven pairs of chromosomes is 7/7 or 1. The allele for the second trait can be carried on any one of the remaining six chromosome pairs and the probability of its being on one of the remaining six (out of a total of 7) is 6/7.

The allele for the third trait can be carried on any of the remaining (a)_____pairs of chromosomes (out of a total of (b)_____ pairs). The probability of this occurring is (c)_____.

The allele for the fourth trait can be carried on any of the remaining (d)_____pairs of chromosomes; the probability of this occurring is (e)_____.

The allele for the fifth trait can be carried on any of the remaining (f)_____pairs of chromosomes; the probability for this occurring is (g)_____.

The allele for the sixth trait can be carried on either of the remaining (h)_____pairs of chromosomes; the probability of this occurring is (i)_____.

The allele for the seventh trait must be carried on the (j)_____ remaining pair of chromosomes. The probability of this occurring is (k)_____.

(a) 5   (d) 4   (g) 3/7   (j) 1
(b) 7   (e) 4/7   (h) 2   (k) 1/7
(c) 5/7   (f) 3   (i) 2/7

46. By using the individual probabilities for each separate trait being carried on a different chromosome, we (multiply/divide)_____ the separate probabilities of the individual events to arrive at the probability of their occurring simultaneously.

Therefore, for the garden pea, the probability of randomly selecting seven different traits, each one of which is carried on a different pair of chromosomes is _____

Multiply;
$7/7 \times 6/7 \times 5/7 \times 4/7 \times 3/7 \times 2/7 \times 1/7 =$
    $5040/823,543 = 720/117,649$ or about 1/163

47. The principle or generalization concerning the probability of two simultaneously occurring independent events is as follows:
The probability of two independent events occurring simultaneously is equal to the probability of the first event (times/plus) _____ *the probability of the second event.*

---

48. Would the above principle apply to the probability of three or more independent events occurring simultaneously?
Yes _____   No _____

Yes (see previous frames).

Section 3: Either-Or—Add

49. You are holding only the King and Queen of Clubs in your hand and a card is drawn from only these two cards.
   (a) What is the probability that the Queen of Clubs will be drawn? _____
   (b) What is the probability that the King of Clubs will be drawn? _____
   (c) What is the probability of drawing either the King or the Queen of Clubs? _____

(a) The probability that the Queen will be drawn is ½.
(b) The probability that the King will be drawn is ½.
(c) The probability of drawing either the King or the Queen is ½ + ½ = 1.

50. (a) The probability of rolling a die and getting a "2" is _____.
   (b) The probability of rolling a die and getting a "6" is _____.
   (c) The probability of rolling a die and getting either a two or a six is _____.

(a) Probability of getting a 2 is 1/6.
(b) Probability of getting a 6 is 1/6.
(c) Probability of getting either a 2 or a 6 is $1/6 + 1/6 = 2/6$ or $1/3$.

51. If a card is drawn from a deck of 52 cards, what is the probability of drawing either a heart or a club?_____

Probability of drawing a heart is 13/52, (1/4).
Probability of drawing a club is 13/52, (1/4).
Probability of drawing either a heart or a club is;
$13/52 + 13/52 = 26/52$ or $1/2$.

52. There are 10 boxes of cracker jacks on a counter. There are prizes in three of the ten boxes—a toy soldier in one, a ring in another, and a stick of gum in a third.
    (a) What is the probability of getting a box with a prize?_____
    (b) What is the probability of getting the box with the ring?_____
    (c) The probability of getting either the ring or the toy soldier?
_____

(a) 3 chances in $10 = 3/10 =$ probability of getting a prize.
(b) 1 chance in $10 = 1/10 =$ probability of getting the ring.
(c) $1/10 + 1/10 = 2/10 = 1/5 =$ probability of getting either the ring or the soldier.

53. A number of marbles are put into a box. There are four different colors of marbles; some are yellow, some green, some blue and some are red. A person, blindfolded, picks a blue marble ¼ of the time, a green marble 3/20 of the time, and a yellow marble 1/5 of the time.

(a) What is the probability of picking a marble that is either yellow, green, red, or blue?_____

(b) What is the probability that the person will pick a red marble?_____

(a) The probability of picking a marble that is either yellow, green, red or blue is 20/20 or 1. There were only these four colors of marbles in the box.

(b)

Prob. of Green		Prob. of Yellow		Prob. of Blue		Prob. of Red		Total Probability
3/20	+	4/20	+	5/20	+	?/20	=	20/20

?/20 = 20/20 - 12/20 = 2/5

Therefore, the probability of picking red = 2/5.

54. If the probability of having type O blood is ½ and the probability of having type A blood is ¼, would you add or multiply the separate probabilities to find the probability of a person having either type O or type A blood?_____

Add

55. If the probability of having type O blood is ½ and the probability of having type A blood is ¼, what is the probability of a person having either type O or type A blood?_____

Probability of Type O Blood		Probability of Type A Blood		Probability of Either O or A
1/2	+	1/4	=	3/4

56. (a) In a particular woods there are eight dead trees—five beech and 3 maple. Three pairs of owls nest in the woods. Each pair nests in a dead tree and no tree contains more than one nest. Assuming the choice of a nesting site is random,

    (1) What is the probability of the first pair nesting in a maple?
    _____

    (2) In a beech?_____
    (3) Either a maple or a beech?_____

(b) If the first pair nested in a maple, what is the probability of the second pair nesting in a:
    (1) Maple?_____
    (2) Beech?

(c) If the first and second pairs nested in maples, what is the probability of the third pair nesting in a:
    (1) Maple?_____
    (2) Beech?_____

(d) What is the probability of all three owl pairs nesting in maples?
_____

(a) (1) 3 chances to nest in a maple out of 8 dead trees $= 3/8$
    (2) 5 chances to nest in a beech out of 8 dead trees $= 5/8$
    (3) $3/8 + 5/8 = 8/8$ or 1

(b) (1) 2 chances to nest in a maple out of 7 dead trees $= 2/7$ (because one pair has nested in a maple, leaving only 7 trees to nest in and only 2 of these are maples).
    (2) 5/7

(c) (1) 1/6
    (2) 5/6

(d)

Probability of First Pair in a Maple		Probability of Second Pair in a Maple		Probability of Third Pair in a Maple	Probability of all 3 Pairs in Maples
3/8	$\times$	2/7	$\times$	1/6	$= 6/336$ or $1/56$

57. The probability of either one event or the other occurring is equal to the (product/sum)＿＿＿＿＿of the individual probabilities.

Sum.

58. You have now learned two basic principles or generalizations which are useful in determining probabilities:

1) The probability of two or more independent events occurring simultaneously is equal to the (sum/product)＿＿＿＿＿＿＿＿＿ of their separate probabilities (see Frame 47).

2) The probability of either one event or the other occurring is equal to the (product/sum)＿＿＿＿＿＿＿ of the individual probabilities (see Frame 57).

These two principles may be combined in determining probabilities, as illustrated in the following problem:

The probability of rolling two dice and:
    (a) getting either a two or a three on the first die is＿＿＿＿＿.
    (b) getting a six on the second die is＿＿＿＿＿＿＿＿＿＿.
    (c) the probability of rolling two dice and getting either a two or a three on the first die and getting a six on the second die is＿＿＿＿＿＿.

(a) The probability of getting a 2 is 1/6.
    The probability of getting a 3 is 1/6.
    The probability of getting either a 2 or a 3 is
    1/6 + 1/6 =2/6 or 1/3.

(b) The probability of getting a 6 on the second die is 1/6.

(c)
Probability of Either a 2 or 3 on First Die		Probability of Getting a 6 on Second Die		Probability for Both
2/6	×	1/6	=	2/36 or 1/18

59. In a family consisting of 2 children, what is the probability of having a boy for the first child and either a boy or a girl for the second child?_____

Probability of having a boy for the first child = ½.
Probability of having either a boy or a girl for the second child = ½ + ½ = 1.

Therefore, the probability of having a boy for the first child and either a boy or a girl for the second child = ½ x 1 = ½.

Progress Quiz—Basic Probability Principles

The answers to these quiz questions are provided only in the Teachers' Manual.

60. Three pennies are simultaneously flipped into the air. How many different possible combinations or orders are there for the three pennies?_____

61. There are 20 commonly occurring amino acids in living organisms. If we know that 10 of these 20 amino acids are not found in a particular dipeptide, how many different dipeptides are possible?_____

62. The probability of an albino being born to parents, both of whom are heterozygous concerning the albino trait, is ¼. What is the probability of their having an albino girl?_____

63. A couple has 2 boys. What is the probability of both of their next two children being boys?_____

64. What is the probability of tossing a die and getting either a "2" or a "4"?_____

65. A number of marbles are put into a box. There are only four colors of marbles. The probability of picking, blindfolded, a blue marble equals 1/4; a green marble equals 3/20; a yellow marble equals 1/5; and a red marble equals 2/5. What is the probability of picking either a yellow or a red marble?_____

66. (a) The probability of either one event or the other occurring at a particular time is equal to the probability of the first event occurring (times/plus) _____ the probability of the second event occurring.
(b) The probability of two independent events occurring simultaneously is equal to the probability of the first event occurring (times/plus) _____ the probability of the second event occurring.

67. In a family of 2 children,
    (a) What is the probability that both will be girls (i.e., GG)? _____
    (b) both boys (BB)?_____
    (c) What is the probability that the first child will be a girl and the second a boy (GB)?_____
    (d) What is the probability that the first child will be a boy and the second a girl (BG)?_____
    (e) What is the probability of having 1 boy and 1 girl in any order?_____
    (f) What is the probability that, in a family of 2 children, there will be either 2 girls (GG), or 2 boys (BB), or a girl and a boy (GB), or a boy and a girl (BG)?_____

68. In a DNA molecule, the probability of getting any of the four nitrogen-containing bases at a particular position equals 1/4. What is the probability of getting either the sequence guanine-alanine-cytosine (GAC), or guanine-guanine-thymine (GGT)? _____

69. Twenty marbles are put into a box. There are four different colors of marbles: 5 yellow, 5 green, 5 blue, and 5 red. A blindfolded person withdraws three marbles and does *not* return them to the box. On his first trial, he picks a green marble.

    (a) What is the probability that, on his second trial, he will pick a green marble?_____

    (b) What is the probability that, on his second trial, he will pick a blue marble?_____

    (c) What is the probability that, on his second trial, he will pick either a blue, a yellow, or a red marble?_____

    (d) If, on his second trial, he picked a green marble, what is the probability of his picking a green marble on his third trial?_____

    (e) What is the probability of his picking 3 green marbles?
_____

II
Binomial Expansion

Section 1: Expanding the Binomial

You will be expected to carry out the following steps in working probability problems in this section of the program.

Step 1.

What is the probability that in a family of 3 children there will be 2 girls and 1 boy? The following steps must be considered when answering this question.

The three possible orders of birth for two girls and one boy in a family of three children are:
> Boy - Girl - Girl (BGG)
> Girl - Boy - Girl (GBG)
> Girl - Girl - Boy (GGB)

First Child		Second Child		Third Child		*Probability of A Family of 3 Children*
Prob. of B		Prob. of G		Prob. of G		consisting of BGG in that order
$\frac{1}{2}$	x	$\frac{1}{2}$	x	$\frac{1}{2}$	=	$\frac{1}{8}$
Prob. of G		Prob. of B		Prob. of G		consisting of GBG in that order
$\frac{1}{2}$	x	$\frac{1}{2}$	x	$\frac{1}{2}$	=	$\frac{1}{8}$
Prob. of G		Prob. of G		Prob. of B		consisting of GGB in that order
$\frac{1}{2}$	x	$\frac{1}{2}$	x	$\frac{1}{2}$	=	$\frac{1}{8}$

Any of these three orders (i.e., *either* BGG, *or* GBG, *or* GGB) is possible for a family of three children consisting of two girls and one boy. Therefore, we *add* the separate probabilities for the various combinations to obtain the probability of a family of three children consisting of two girls and one boy in any order.

Probability of BGG		*Probability of GBG*		*Probability GGB*		*Probability of 2G and 1B in Any Order*
¹⁄₈	+	¹⁄₈	+	¹⁄₈	=	³⁄₈

Note, the probability for two boys and one girl (BBB, BGB, GBB) is the same, i.e., ³⁄₈. However, the probability of three girls (GGG) equals ¹⁄₈ because there is only <u>one order</u> in which we can have 3 girls:

Probability of a Girl		*Probability of a Girl*		*Probability of a Girl*		*Probability of GGG*
¹⁄₂	x	¹⁄₂	x	¹⁄₂	=	¹⁄₈

Likewise, the probability of three boys (i.e., BBB) equals ¹⁄₈.

70. Recall that there are *four* different nitrogen-containing bases that may occur in the nucleotides that make up the DNA molecule.
   (a) What is the probability that any *one* of the four bases will occur at a particular position? _____
   (b) In a three-nucleotide sequence, what are the possible combinations of 2 guanine molecules (G) and 1 adenine molecule (A)? _____
   (c) What is the probability of 2 guanine and 1 adenine occurring in that sequence (GGA)? _____
   (d) What is the probability of the sequence GAG? _____
   (e) What is the probability of the sequence AGG? _____
   (f) What is the probability that in a three-nucleotide sequence the bases will be 2G and 1A in any order? _____

(a) The probability of one of the four possible bases occurring at a given position in the nucleotide sequence is ¹⁄₄

(b) The possible combinations are: GGA, GAG, AGG
(c) The probability of the sequence GGA $= \frac{1}{4} \times \frac{1}{4} \times \frac{1}{4} = \frac{1}{64}$.
(d) The probability of the sequence GAG $= \frac{1}{4} \times \frac{1}{4} \times \frac{1}{4} = \frac{1}{64}$.
(e) The probability of the sequence AGG $= \frac{1}{4} \times \frac{1}{4} \times \frac{1}{4} = \frac{1}{64}$.
(f) The probability of having 2 guanine and 1 adenine in a three-base sequence equals $\frac{1}{64} + \frac{1}{64} + \frac{1}{64} = \frac{3}{64}$.

71. In a family of 4 children, 3 are girls and 1 is a boy.
    (a) What are the possible orders of birth of girls and boys for this family?_____
    (b) What is the probability of the birth order BGGG?_____
    (c) of the birth order GBGG?_____
    (d) of the birth order GGBG?_____
    (e) of the birth order GGGB?_____
    (f) What is the probability that, in a family of 4 children, 3 will be girls and 1 will be a boy?_____

(a) The possible birth orders are: BGGG, GBGG, GGBG, GGGB
(b) The probability of BGGG $= \frac{1}{2} \times \frac{1}{2} \times \frac{1}{2} \times \frac{1}{2} = \frac{1}{16}$
(c) The probability of GBGG $= \frac{1}{2} \times \frac{1}{2} \times \frac{1}{2} \times \frac{1}{2} = \frac{1}{16}$
(d) The probability of GGBG $= \frac{1}{2} \times \frac{1}{2} \times \frac{1}{2} \times \frac{1}{2} = \frac{1}{16}$
(e) The probability of GGGB $= \frac{1}{2} \times \frac{1}{2} \times \frac{1}{2} \times \frac{1}{2} = \frac{1}{16}$
(f)

Prob. of BGGG		Prob. of GBGG		Prob. of GGBG		Prob. of GGGB		Prob. of 3G + 1B in Any Order
$\frac{1}{16}$	+	$\frac{1}{16}$	+	$\frac{1}{16}$	+	$\frac{1}{16}$	=	$\frac{4}{16}$ or $\frac{1}{4}$

72. In a family of 4 children
    (a) What is the probability that all 4 will be boys?_____
    (b) all 4 will be girls?_____

(a) *Prob. of*   *Prob. of*   *Prob. of*   *Prob. of*   *Prob. of*
    A Boy   *A Boy*   *A Boy*   *A Boy*   *4 Boys*
    ½ x   ½ x   ½ x   ½ =   ¹⁄₁₆

(b) Likewise, the probability of 4 girls = $\frac{1}{16}$

73. A card is drawn from a deck of 52 playing cards.
    (a) What is the probability that this card will be a heart?_____
    (b) What is the probability that it will be a spade?_____

(a) The probability of drawing a heart is $13/52$ or $1/4$
(b) The probability of drawing a spade is $13/52$ or $1/4$

74. Four cards are drawn, each from a *different* deck of 52 cards.
    (a) Assuming that 3 hearts (H) and 1 spade (S) are drawn, what are the different orders in which they can occur?_____

    (b) What is the probability that 3 of the cards will be hearts and one of them will be a spade in any order?_____

(a) The 3 hearts and 1 spade can be drawn in these four different orders: HHHS, HHSH, HSHH, SHHH.
(b) The probability of HHHS
    $= 13/52 \times 13/52 \times 13/52 \times 13/52 = 1/256$
    or (¼)   (¼)   (¼)   (¼)
    The probability of HHSH $= 1/4 \times 1/4 \times 1/4 \times 1/4 = 1/256$
    The probability of HSHH $= 1/4 \times 1/4 \times 1/4 \times 1/4 = 1/256$
    The probability of SHHH $= 1/4 \times 1/4 \times 1/4 \times 1/4 = 1/256$
    The probability of drawing three hearts and one spade in any order $= 1/256 + 1/256 + 1/256 + 1/256 = 4/256$ or $1/64$

75. In a family of 5 children:
   - (a) How many different orders of birth are there for 3 boys and 2 girls?_____
   - (b) What are these different orders?_____

   _____

   - (c) What is the probability for any *one* particular order of birth of the ten possible orders?_____
   - (d) In a family of 5 children, what is the probability of having 3 boys and 2 girls in any order?_____

_____

(a) There are 10 possible orders of birth for 3 boys and 2 girls in a family consisting of 5 children.

(b) These orders are: BBBGG, BBGGB, BGGBB, GGBBB, GBBBG, BBGBG, BGBGB, BGBBG, GBBGB, GBGBB.

(c) The probability for any *one* of the ten possible orders is $1/32$; i.e.,

Prob. of BBBGG is $1/2 \times 1/2 \times 1/2 \times 1/2 \times 1/2 = 1/32$
Prob. of BBGGB is $1/2 \times 1/2 \times 1/2 \times 1/2 \times 1/2 = 1/32$
Prob. of BGGBB is $1/2 \times 1/2 \times 1/2 \times 1/2 \times 1/2 = 1/32$
Prob. of GGBBB is $1/2 \times 1/2 \times 1/2 \times 1/2 \times 1/2 = 1/32$
Prob. of GBBBG is $1/2 \times 1/2 \times 1/2 \times 1/2 \times 1/2 = 1/32$
Prob. of BBGBG is $1/2 \times 1/2 \times 1/2 \times 1/2 \times 1/2 = 1/32$
Prob. of BGBGB is $1/2 \times 1/2 \times 1/2 \times 1/2 \times 1/2 = 1/32$
Prob. of BGBBG is $1/2 \times 1/2 \times 1/2 \times 1/2 \times 1/2 = 1/32$
Prob. of GBBGB is $1/2 \times 1/2 \times 1/2 \times 1/2 \times 1/2 = 1/32$
Prob. of GBGBB is $1/2 \times 1/2 \times 1/2 \times 1/2 \times 1/2 = 1/32$

(d) The probability of having 3 boys and 2 girls in any order is
$1/32 + 1/32 + 1/32 + 1/32 + 1/32 + 1/32 + 1/32 + 1/32 + 1/32 + 1/32 =$
$10/32$ or $5/16$

76. In a family of 5 children, what is the probability of having *2 boys* and *3 girls* in any order?_____

_____

The probability of having 3 girls and 2 boys in a family of 5 children is $10/32$ or $5/16$. (For explanation, see Frame 75.)

77. In a family of 5 children:
   (a) How many different orders of birth are there for 4 boys and 1 girl? _____
   (b) What are these different orders? _____
   _____
   (c) What is the probability for any *one* particular order of birth of the five possible orders?_____
   (d) In a family of 5 children, what is the probability of having 4 boys and 1 girl in any order?_____

_____

(a) There are 5 possible orders of birth for 4 boys and 1 girl in a family consisting of 5 children.
(b) These different orders are: BBBBG, BBBGB, BBGBB, BGBBB, GBBBB.
(c) The probability of any one of the five different orders is $1/32$; i.e.,
   Prob. of BBBBG is $1/2 \times 1/2 \times 1/2 \times 1/2 \times 1/2 = 1/32$
   Prob. of BBBGB is $1/2 \times 1/2 \times 1/2 \times 1/2 \times 1/2 = 1/32$
   Prob. of BBGBB is $1/2 \times 1/2 \times 1/2 \times 1/2 \times 1/2 = 1/32$
   Prob. of BGBBB is $1/2 \times 1/2 \times 1/2 \times 1/2 \times 1/2 = 1/32$
   Prob. of GBBBB is $1/2 \times 1/2 \times 1/2 \times 1/2 \times 1/2 = 1/32$
(d) The probability of having 4 boys and 1 girl in any order is $1/32 + 1/32 + 1/32 + 1/32 + 1/32 = 5/32$.

78. In a family of 5 children, what is the probability of having *4 girls* and *1 boy* in any order?_____

_____

The probability of having 4 girls and 1 boy in a family of 5 children equals $5/32$. (For explanation, see Frame 77 above.)

79. In a family of 5 children:
   (a) What is the probability that all 5 children will be boys?_____

   (b) all 5 children will be girls?_____

(a) Since there is *only one* order of 5 boys (i.e., BBBBB), the probability that all 5 children will be boys is $\frac{1}{2} \times \frac{1}{2} \times \frac{1}{2} \times \frac{1}{2} \times \frac{1}{2} = \frac{1}{32}$.
(b) Likewise, the probability that all 5 children will be girls is $\frac{1}{32}$.

80. The answers for the 5 preceding frames (i.e., Frames 75-79) may be worked out much more easily in another way known as *expansion of the binomial.* We will now investigate this method.

A binomial has two terms: "a" (which represents the probability of one event) and "b" (which represents the probability of the alternative event). To expand the binomial, we "raise" it to specific *powers*, depending on the number of "events" involved in the particular problem. For example, we can have $(a + b)^2$, $(a + b)^3$, $(a + b)^4$, etc. In other words, the binomial can be shown as $(a + b)^N$, where N = _____

The total number of events we are considering.

81. The binomial expansion principle can be used in working probability problems *only* when the sum of the probabilities of the events is equal to one. Therefore, $(a + b)$ is always equal to _____

One.

82. To "expand" the binomial $(a + b)^2$ we multiply $(a + b)$ times $(a + b)$. What is the product obtained when you expand the binomial $(a + b)^2$?_____

$a^2 + 2ab + b^2$
If you got this correct, go to Frame 84.
If you *did not* get this answer correct, go to frame 83.

83. The product of $(a + b)^2$ may be obtained as follows:
$(a + b)^2 = (a + b) \times (a + b)$
This may be written with one term above the other for ease in doing the multiplication.

  $(a + b)$
$\underline{\times (a + b)}$

We multiply each term of each binomial by each term of the other binomial. Starting with the "b" of the lower binomial,
"b" x "b" $= b^2$ and "b" x "a" $= ab$. In the problem, this appears as:

  $(a + b)$
$\underline{\times (a + b)}$
  $ab + b^2$

Now, taking the "a" of the lower binomial,
"a" x "a" $= a^2$ and "a" x "b" $= ab$. The problem now appears as:

    $(a + b)$
  $\underline{\times (a + b)}$
    $ab + b^2$
$a^2 + ab$

We now add to get the final product. Therefore, the expansion of $(a + b)^2$ is: (Write the answer in the box below)

    $(a + b)$
  $\underline{\times (a + b)}$
    $ab + b^2$
$a^2 + ab$

┌─────────────────────┐
│   │
│   │
└─────────────────────┘

$a^2 + 2ab + b^2$
If you did not get this correct, re-study frame 83.

84. Expand the binomial $(a + b)^3$. The product obtained is_____.
    _____

$a^3 + 3a^2b + 3ab^2 + b^3$
If you got this correct, go to frame 86.
If you *did not* get this answer correct, go to frame 85.

85. The product of $(a + b)^3$ may be obtained as follows:
$$(a + b)^3 = (a + b) \times (a + b) \times (a + b).$$

$$
\begin{array}{r}
(a + b) \\
\times\, (a + b) \\
\hline
ab + b^2 \\
a^2 + ab \\
\hline
a^2 + 2ab + b^2 \\
(a + b) \\
\hline
a^2b + 2ab^2 + b^3 \\
a^3 + 2a^2b + ab^2 \\
\hline
\end{array}
$$

However, since you already have expanded $(a + b)^2$, it might be easier to expand $(a + b)^3$ in the following way:

$$
\begin{array}{l}
(a + b)^3 = (a + b)^2 \times (a + b) \\
(a + b)^2 = a^2 + 2ab + b^2 \\
(a + b) \\
\hline
a^2b + 2ab^2 + b^3 \\
a^3 + 2a^2b + ab^2 \\
\hline
\end{array}
$$

The product for both problems is: $a^3 + 3a^2b + 3ab^2 + b^3$.

86. Now, expand the binomial $(a + b)^4$. Remember, $(a + b)^4 =$ $(a + b) \times (a + b) \times (a + b) \times (a + b)$. The product obtained when you expand the binomial $(a + b)^4$ is _____

$(a + b)^4 = a^4 + 4a^3b + 6a^2b^2 + 4ab^3 + b^4$.
If you got this correct, go to frame 88.
If you *did not* get this correct, go to frame 87.

87. A. The product of $(a + b)^4 =$

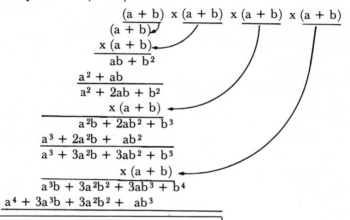

B. Or we can work it this way:

$(a + b)^4 = (a + b)^2 \times (a + b)^2$.

$(a + b)^2 =$ _____

Therefore, $\underline{(a + b)^2} \times \underline{(a + b)^2}$

_____

x _____

_____

$(a + b)^4 =$

A. The product of $(a + b)^4 = a^4 + 4a^3b + 6a^2b^2 + 4ab^3 + b^4$;

B. $(a + b)^2 = a^2 + 2ab + b^2$;

Therefore:

$$
\begin{array}{r}
a^2 + 2ab + b^2 \\
\times\ a^2 + 2ab + b^2 \\
\hline
a^2b^2 + 2ab^3 + b^4 \\
2a^3b + 4a^2b^2 + 2ab^3 \\
a^4 + 2a^3b + a^2b^2 \\
\hline
a^4 + 4a^3b + 6a^2b^2 + 4ab^3 + b^4 = (a + b)^4.
\end{array}
$$

88. Expand the binomial $(a + b)^5$. The product of $(a + b)^5$ is _____

_____

_____

$a^5 + 5a^4b + 10a^3b^2 + 10a^2b^3 + 5ab^4 + b^5 = (a + b)^5$

If you got this correct, go to frame 90.

If you *did not* get this correct, go to frame 89.

89. Expansion of $(a + b)^5 =$

$(a + b) \times (a + b) \times (a + b) \times (a + b) \times (a + b) = \underline{(a + b)^3} \times \underline{(a + b)^2}$

_____

x _____

_____

$(a + b)^5 =$

_____

$$(a + b)^5 = (a + b)^3 \text{ x } (a + b)^2$$

$$\begin{array}{rl}
(a + b)^3 = & a^3 + 3a^2b + 3ab^2 + b^3 \\
(a + b)^2 = & \underline{x \qquad a^2 + 2ab + b^2} \\
& a^3b^2 + 3a^2b^3 + 3ab^4 + b^5 \\
& 2a^4b + 6a^3b^2 + 6a^2b^3 + 2ab^4 \\
& \underline{a^5 + 3a^4b + 3a^3b^2 + a^2b^3} \\
\end{array}$$

$$(a + b)^5 = a^5 + 5a^4b + 10a^3b^2 + 10a^2b^3 + 5ab^4 + b^5$$

90. We are now prepared to use this binomial expansion principle in solving probability problems. In the binomial $(a + b)^N$, let "a" equal the probability of one event occurring and let "b" equal the probability of the alternative event occurring. We will consider a family of 3 children.

    (a) Remember, N = _____ .

    (b) In this case, N = _____ .

    (c) The probability of having a girl ("a") plus the probability of having a boy ("b") must equal _____ .

(a) the total number of events we are considering.

(b) the 3 children or 3.

(c) one.

91. Since we are considering 3 events or children, we will use the expanded binomial $(a + b)^3$. Remember, "a" is the probability of having a girl $= \frac{1}{2}$ and "b" is the probability of having a boy $= \frac{1}{2}$. $(a + b) = (\frac{1}{2} + \frac{1}{2}) = 1$. From the expanded binomial $(a + b)^3$ $= \boxed{a^3} + 3a^2b + 3ab^2 + b^3$

The first term, a^3 , may be interpreted as follows:

    The "a" = the probability of the first event, in this case, the probability of having a girl; the superscript 3 (cube symbol, "3"), means that "a" is multiplied times "a" times "a". In this case, the a^3 would give us the probability of having 3 girls in a family of 3 children.

What is the probability of having 3 girls in a family of 3 children?

For finding the probability of having 3 girls in a family of 3 children we must substitute the probability of having a girl $= \frac{1}{2}$ for "a" and since we are concerned with the probability of 3 girls, the term we use is a^3.

Therefore, $a^3 = (\frac{1}{2})^3$ or $\frac{1}{8} =$ the probability of having 3 girls in a family of 3 children.

92. From the expanded binomial $(a + b)^3 = a^3 + 3a^2b + 3ab^2 + b^3$ the second term, $3a^2b$, may be interpreted as follows:

> The coefficient, 3, indicates that there are 3 possible combinations or order of events. In this case, there are 3 different orders of birth for one boy and two girls. The "a" is the probability of having a girl and "b" is the probability of having a boy. The superscript "2" of the "a" in the term $3a^2b$, refers to having 2 girls and the superscript "1" (understood) of the "b" refers to having 1 boy. Note that the sum of the exponents $(2 + 1)$ equals the total number of events (children).

In a family of 3 children, what is the probability of having 2 girls and 1 boy in any order?_____

The term we are interested in is $3a^2b$. Now, substitute the probability of having a girl $= \frac{1}{2}$ for "a" and the probability of having a boy $= \frac{1}{2}$ for "b". Therefore: $3a^2b =$
$3(\frac{1}{2})^2$ x $(\frac{1}{2}) =$
3 x $\frac{1}{2}$ x $\frac{1}{2}$ x $\frac{1}{2} = \frac{3}{8} =$ the probability of having 2 girls and 1 boy in a family of 3 children.

93. From the expanded binomial $(a + b)^3 = a^3 + 3a^2b + \boxed{3ab^2} + b^3$ the third term, $3ab^2$, may be interpreted as follows:

> The coefficient, 3, indicates that there are 3 possible combinations or orders of events. In this case, there are 3 different orders of birth for two boys and one girl. The "a" is the probability of having a girl and "b" is the probability of having a boy. The superscript "1" (understood) of the "a" refers to having 1 girl and the superscript "2" of the "b" refers to having 2 boys.

In a family of 3 children, what is the probability of having 1 girl and 2 boys in any order? _____

The term we are interested in is $3ab^2$. Substituting ½ for "a" and ½ for "b" we have:

$3ab^2 =$

$3(½) \times (½)^2 =$

$3 \times ½ \times ½ \times ½ = ⅜ =$ the probability of having 1 girl and 2 boys in a family of 3 children.

94. From the expanded binomial $(a + b)^3 = a^3 + 3a^2b + 3ab^2 + \boxed{b^3}$ the last term may be interpreted as follows:

> The "b" = the probability of the alternative event, in this case, the probability of having a boy; the superscript "3" means that "b" is multiplied times "b" times "b". In this case, the b^3 would give us the probability of having 3 boys in a family of 3 children.

What is the probability of having 3 boys in a family of 3 children?

The term we are interested in is b^3. Substituting the probability of having a boy = ½ for "b" we have:

$b^3 = (½)^3$ or $⅛ =$ the probability of having 3 boys in a family of 3 children.

95. From the expansion of the binomial, $(a + b)^5$:
   (a) which term represents the probability of having 5 girls in a family consisting of 5 children?_____
   (b) what is the probability of having 5 girls in a family consisting of 5 children?_____

(a) Expansion of the binomial $(a + b)^5$ equals $a^5 + 5a^4b + 10a^3b^2 + 10a^2b^3 + 5ab^4 + b^5$. The term which represents the probability of having 5 girls in a family of 5 children is a^5, where "a" represents the probability of having a girl $= \frac{1}{2}$; the superscript or exponent, 5, means 5 girls.

(b) The probability of having 5 girls in a family of 5 children can be found quickly by substituting the probability of a girl $= \frac{1}{2}$ for "a". Therefore:
$a^5 = \frac{1}{2} \times \frac{1}{2} \times \frac{1}{2} \times \frac{1}{2} \times \frac{1}{2} = \frac{1}{32}$

96. From the expansion of the binomial, $(a + b)^5$:
   (a) which term represents the probability of having 5 boys in a family consisting of 5 children?_____
   (b) What is the probability of having 5 boys in a family consisting of 5 children?_____
   (c) Which term represents the probability of having 4 girls and 1 boy in any order?_____
   (d) In a family of 5 children, what is the probability of having 4 girls and 1 boy in any order?_____

(a) Expansion of the binomial $(a + b)^5 =$ $a^5 + 5a^4b + 10a^3b^2 + 10a^2b^3 + 5ab^4 + b^5$. The term which represents the probability of having 5 boys in a family of 5 children is b^5, where "b" represents the probability of having a boy $= \frac{1}{2}$; the exponent, 5, means 5 boys.

(b) The probability of having 5 boys in a family consisting of 5 children $= b^5 = (\frac{1}{2})^5 = \frac{1}{2} \times \frac{1}{2} \times \frac{1}{2} \times \frac{1}{2} \times \frac{1}{2} = \frac{1}{32}$.

(c) The term which represents the probability of having 4 girls and 1 boy in any order is $5a^4b$, where "a" represents the probability of a girl $= \frac{1}{2}$ and the exponent, 4, means 4 girls. The "b" represents the probability of a boy $= \frac{1}{2}$ and the exponent, 1 (understood), means 1 boy. The coefficient, 5, means there are 5 different orders or combinations of 4 girls and 1 boy for a family of 5 children.

(d) In a family of 5 children, the probability of having 4 girls and 1 boy in any order is:

$5a^4b = 5(\frac{1}{2})^4 \times (\frac{1}{2}) =$

$5 \times \frac{1}{2} \times \frac{1}{2} \times \frac{1}{2} \times \frac{1}{2} \times \frac{1}{2} = \frac{5}{32}$.

97. In a family consisting of 5 children, what is the probability of having 1 girl and 4 boys in any order?_____

The term of the expanded binomial $(a + b)^5$ that we are interested in is $5ab^4$, which represents the probability of having 1 girl and 4 boys in a family of 5 children. Substituting, we get:

$5ab^4 = 5(\frac{1}{2}) \times (\frac{1}{2})^4 =$

$5 \times \frac{1}{2} \times \frac{1}{2} \times \frac{1}{2} \times \frac{1}{2} \times \frac{1}{2} = \frac{5}{32}$.

98. In a family consisting of 5 children,
(a) What is the probability of having 3 girls and 2 boys?
_____

(b) What is the probability of having 2 girls and 3 boys?
_____

(a) The term of the expanded binomial, $(a + b)^5$, that we are interested in is $10a^3b^2$, where the coefficient, 10, represents the

10 different orders in which there can be 3 girls and 2 boys in a family of 5 children. Substituting, we get:

$10a^3b^2 = 10 \; (½)^3 \; x \; (½)^2 =$

$10 \; x \; ½ \; x \; ½ \; x \; ½ \; x \; ½ \; x \; ½ = {}^{10}/_{32} =$ the probability of having 3 girls and 2 boys in a family of 5 children.

(b) The term which represents the probability of having 2 girls and 3 boys in a family of 5 children is $10a^2b^3$. Substituting, the probability equals:

$10a^2b^3 = 10 \; (½)^2 \; x \; (½)^3 =$

$10 \; x \; ½ \; x \; ½ \; x \; ½ \; x \; ½ \; x \; ½ = {}^{10}/_{32}$

99. Two individuals, both heterozygous for the gene D, are mated. The probability of the offspring showing the dominant gene, D (= "a"), is ¾. The probability of the offspring showing the recessive gene, d (= "b"), is ¼. Using the binomial expansion method, calculate the probability that, in a family of 5 children, 3 of them will express the D gene and 2 of them, the d gene.

Since we are concerned with 5 events (i.e., 3 offspring expressing D plus 2 offspring expressing d), we expand the binomial $(a + b)^5$ to give: $a^5 + 5a^4b + 10a^3b^2 + 10a^2b^3 + 5ab^4 + b^5$.

The term we want is $10a^3b^2$ because there are 10 different orders in which there could be 3 children showing the dominant gene D and 2 children showing the recessive gene d. Substituting the probability, $¾ = a =$ the probability of expressing D and $¼ = b =$ the probability of expressing d, we get:

$10a^3b^2 = 10 \; x \; (¾)^3 \; x \; (¼)^2 =$

$10 \; x \; 3/4 \; x \; 3/4 \; x \; 3/4 \; x \; 1/4 \; x \; 1/4 = 270/1024$ or $135/512$ or about $1/3.79$.

100. At this time we can introduce short cuts for finding the exponents and coefficients in expanding the binomial.

Perhaps the short cut for the determination of exponents is already obvious.

(a) Expand the binomial $(a + b)^5$.

    Note that as the exponent of a "a" decreases, the exponent of "b" increases. The exponent of "a" always begins with the number which equals the N value, and decreases to 1 (which is understood), and finally to 0. It should be mentioned that $a^0 = 1$. Likewise, $b^0 = 1$. However, note that in each term the sum of the exponents of "a" and "b" equals the N value, in this case, 5.

(b) Therefore, in the binomial $(a + b)^5$, "a" and its exponents progress as follows:

a^5,_____,_____,_____,_____, a^0 or 1.

(c) "b" and its exponents progress from b^0 or 1,_____,_____, _____,_____,_____.

(a) $a^5 + 5a^4b + 10a^3b^2 + 10a^2b^3 + 5ab^4 + b^5$
(b) a^4, a^3, a^2, a^1 or a
(c) b^1 or b, b^2, b^3, b^4, b^5.

101. Expand the binomial $(a + b)^6$, showing "a" and "b" with their exponents only. (Do not be concerned at this time about the coefficients.)

$a^6 + a^5b + a^4b^2 + a^3b^3 + a^2b^4 + ab^5 + b^6$

102. Now we can concentrate on a short cut for determining the coefficients. Consider the expansion of $(a + b)^5$ again. The coefficient of the first term (in this case a^5) is always 1. Usually, the

1 is not written but is understood. The coefficient of the second term is determined by:

  (a) multiplying the coefficient of the first term (which is always_____) by the exponent of "a" of the first term, which in this case is_____. This gives us_____.

  (b) We then divide this value by the number of the preceding term in the expansion, which in this case is one. Therefore, the coefficient of the second term is_____.

(a) one; five; $1 \times 5 = 5$
(b) $5 \div 1 = 5$

---

103. The succeeding coefficients are determined by employing the same method as you have just used. *That is, the coefficient for any particular term is equal to the product of the coefficient and the exponent of "a" of the preceding term divided by the number of the preceding term in the expanded binomial.* To illustrate, from the expanded binomial $(a + b)^5$, the coefficient of the third term may be obtained as follows:

Coefficient of Preceding Term		Exponent of "a" of Preceding Term		Number of Preceding Term		Desired Coefficient
5	$\times$	4	$\div$	2	$=$	10

That is, the coefficient of the third term = _____

10.

---

104. Now, complete the binomial expansion of $(a + b)^5$, calculating the coefficients of the various terms by the method just explained.

Number of Desired Coefficient	Coefficient of Preceding Term		Exponent of "a" of Preceding Term		Number of Preceding Term		Desired Coefficient
fourth	_____	x	_____	÷	_____	=	_____
fifth	_____	x	_____	÷	_____	=	_____
sixth	_____	x	_____	÷	_____	=	_____

The coefficient of the fourth term is: $10 \times 3 \div 3 = 10$
The coefficient of the fifth term is: $10 \times 2 \div 4 = 5$
The coefficient of the sixth term is: $5 \times 1 \div 5 = 1$

105. Expand the binomial $(a + b)^4$ using the short cuts for determining the exponents and coefficients.

The exponents of the expanded binomial $(a + b)^4$ are:
$a^4 + a^3b + a^2b^2 + ab^3 + b^4$
The coefficients are:
The first coefficient $= 1$.

Number of Desired Coefficient	Coefficient of Preceding Term		Exponent of "a" of Preceding Term		Number of Preceding Term		Desired Coefficient
second	1	x	4	÷	1	=	4
third	4	x	3	÷	2	=	6
fourth	6	x	2	÷	3	=	4
fifth	4	x	1	÷	4	=	1

Therefore, the expanded binomial $(a + b)^4 =$
$a^4 + 4a^3b + 6a^2b^2 + 4ab^3 + b^4$

106. Expand the binomial $(a + b)^6$ using the short cuts for determining the exponents and coefficients.

The exponents of the expanded binomial $(a + b)^6$ are:
$a^6 + a^5b + a^4b^2 + a^3b^3 + a^2b^4 + ab^5 + b^6$.
The coefficient of the first term $= 1$.

Number of Desired Coefficient	Coefficient of Preceding Term		Exponent of "a" of Preceding Term		Number of Preceding Term		Desired Coeffi-cient
second	1	x	6	÷	1	=	6
third	6	x	5	÷	2	=	15
fourth	15	x	4	÷	3	=	20
fifth	20	x	3	÷	4	=	15
sixth	15	x	2	÷	5	=	6
seventh	6	x	1	÷	6	=	1

Therefore, the expanded binomial $(a + b)^6 =$
$a^6 + 6a^5b + 15a^4b^2 + 20a^3b^3 + 15a^2b^4 + 6ab^5 + b^6$.

107. (a) To summarize, a quick method of determining the specific total probability for 2 alternative events which occur a number of times in a number of ways or orders is to use _____.

(b) However, before we can use this method we must first determine the probability of the one event and the probability of _____.

(c) We must also remember that the probability of the first event (times/plus)_____the probability of the alternative event must equal _____.

(a) the binomial expansion principle.
(b) the alternative event.
(c) plus; one.

Progress Quiz—Expanding the Binomial

The answers to these quiz questions are provided in the Teachers' Manual.

108. A couple has 3 children. You are asked to calculate various probabilities concerning the different orders of birth for these 3 children. If you use the binomial expansion principle, you would expand the binomial (a + b) to the _____ power.

109. A couple has 3 children. Which term of the appropriate binomial expansion would represent the probability of their having 1 girl and 2 boys in any order?_____

110. (a) $10a^3b^2$ represents a term in the expanded binomial (a + b) to what power?_____ The probability of one event occurring is represented by _____. The probability of the alternative event occurring is represented by
    (b) The number of times the event having probability "a" occurs, equals _____, (the exponent of "a").
    (c) The exponent of _____ (^{2}), equals
    _____.
    (d) The coefficient, 10, equals the_____of possible ways in which you could have a^3 and b^2.

111. Expand the binomial $(a +b)^5$ showing "a" and "b" with their *exponents* only. Use the short cut method. _____

The probability of a red = "a" = $\frac{1}{4}$.
The probability of a roan or white = "b" = $\frac{1}{2} + \frac{1}{4} = \frac{3}{4}$.
Expanding the binomial $(a + b)^5$, we use the term $10a^2b^3$ and substitute:
$10 \times (\frac{1}{4})^2 \times (\frac{3}{4})^3 = 10 \times \frac{1}{4} \times \frac{1}{4} \times \frac{3}{4} \times \frac{3}{4} \times \frac{3}{4} =$
$270/1024 = 135/512$ or about $1/3.79$.

117. For summer squash, the white fruit, W, is dominant over the colored fruit, w, and disc-shaped fruit, S, is dominant over sphere-shaped fruit, s. If two plants, both heterozygous for both genes, are crossed (i.e., $WwSs$ x $WwSs$), the probability of getting a pure dominant genotype ($WWSS$) is $\frac{1}{16}$ and the probability of getting any other genotype is $\frac{15}{16}$. If a cross like the one described above is made, what is the probability of getting 7 consecutive squash with the pure dominant genotype? _____

If we expand the binomial $(a + b)^7$ we get
$a^7 + 7a^6b + 21a^5b^2 + 35a^4b^3 + 35a^3b^4 + 21a^2b^5 + 7ab^6 + b^7$.
The probability of obtaining a squash plant with the homozygous dominant genotype = "a" = $\frac{1}{16}$. The term we are interested in is the first term in the binomial expansion, a^7. Therefore, we have
$a^7 = (\frac{1}{16})^7 = \frac{1}{16} \times \frac{1}{16} \times \frac{1}{16} \times \frac{1}{16} \times \frac{1}{16} \times \frac{1}{16} \times \frac{1}{16} = 1/268,435,456 =$
the probability of seven consecutive squash with the pure dominant genotype from the dihybrid cross, $WwSs$ x $WwSs$.

118. In pea plants, W represents the gene for round seeds and w is the allele meaning wrinkled seeds. Y represents the gene for yellow seeds and y, the allele for green seeds. If a green-wrinkled plant ($yyww$) is crossed with a yellow-round plant ($YYWW$), F_1 hybrids having the genotype ($YyWw$) are produced. If a hybrid is self-pollinated, the expected phenotypic ratio in the F_2 generation is:
$\frac{9}{16}$ yellow-round
$\frac{3}{16}$ yellow-wrinkled
$\frac{3}{16}$ green-round
$\frac{1}{16}$ green wrinkled
A $YyWw$ hybrid is self-pollinated and 8 seeds are produced. What is the probability of obtaining 4 green-wrinkled seeds among these 8? _____

Here, the probability of getting green-wrinkled = "a" = $\frac{1}{16}$ and the probability of getting anything else = "b" = $\frac{15}{16}$. We expand the binomial $(a + b)^8$ to get:
$$a^8 + 8a^7b + 28a^6b^2 + 56a^5b^3 + 70a^4b^4 + 56a^3b^5 + 28a^2b^6 + 8ab^7 + b^8$$

The term we are interested in is $70a^4b^4$. We substitute
$70a^4b^4 = 70 \times (\frac{1}{16})^4 \times (\frac{15}{16})^4 =$
$70 \times \frac{1}{16} \times \frac{1}{16} \times \frac{1}{16} \times \frac{1}{16} \times \frac{15}{16} \times \frac{15}{16} \times \frac{15}{16} \times \frac{15}{16} =$
$3,543,750/4,294,967,296 = $ about $1/1212$.

Progress Quiz—Using the Binomial Expansion Principle in Calculating Probabilities

The answers to these quiz questions are provided in the Teachers' Manual.

119. (a) The expansion of the binomial $(a + b)$, to the Nth power can be used in calculating probabilities when the two terms of the binomial are probability values, the sum of which is_____
    (b) The exponent, N, represents_____

120. In a litter of nine kittens, what is the probability of having 4 males and 5 females, in any order?_____.

121. In the previous problem you saw that there are 126 different orders in which one can obtain a litter of 9 kittens, consisting of 4 males and 5 females. One of the 126 possible orders is to have 4 males born followed by 5 females. Now, in a litter of 9 kittens, what is the probability of getting 4 males and 5 females, *in that order?*_____

122. In shorthorn cattle, *R* represents the gene which denotes red coat color; *r* represents the gene which denotes white coat color. If an individual is heterozygous, *Rr,* both genes are expressed resulting in a roan coat color. If a roan male is crossed with a roan female, the expected results are:

¼ of offspring will be *RR* -- red coat color

½ of offspring will be *Rr* -- roan coat color

¼ of offspring will be *rr* -- white coat color

Five such matings of roan x roan cattle were made, and five offspring were produced. What is the probability that among these five offspring, 4 will be red and 1 will be either roan or white (i.e., non-red)? _____

III

The Chi-Square Test

123. What is the chi-square test and when is it used? Up to this time we have unconsciously assumed that the deviations from predicted results were due to chance alone. However, there are times when they are *not* due to chance.

"Chi-square" is a statistical test or procedure in which observed results are compared with theoretical expectations to determine whether the observed deviations from predicted results are due to chance alone, or whether the deviations are due to some other factor. For example, if matings of female mice with males of a particular strain resulted in abnormally large numbers of female offspring, one might reasonably question whether or not these results were due to chance alone. By use of the chi-square test to compare the observed results (number of female vs. male offspring) with the expected results (one would expect half of the offspring to be males and half to be females), one could determine the probability of the observed deviations occurring due to chance alone. In other words, chi-square is a test used to determine the probability that observed data are an example of a particular hypothesized result.

To summarize, the chi-square test may be used when we wish to determine whether observed deviations from expected results are due to _____ alone or to some other factor.

---

chance

124. "χ" is the Greek letter chi and is the symbol used to represent this particular statistical test. Therefore, χ^2 stands for_____

χ^2 stands for chi-square

125. Whenever we are determining χ^2, we will always have at least two terms because there will be at least two alternatives that could have been observed; i.e. heads or tails; boys or girls; red, roan, or white (cattle); yellow-round, yellow-wrinkled, green-round, or green-wrinkled (peas).

The χ^2 value is determined by using the following equations:
$$\chi^2 = \Sigma \frac{(O - E)^2}{E}.$$

In this equation the Greek letter sigma, Σ, means "the sum of all"; "O" represents the observed results; and "E" represents the corresponding expected results.
    (a) From the equation above, (O - E) means _____
    _____ .
    (b) The superscript, ^{2} means _____ .

(a) (O - E) means the observed results minus the corresponding expected results.
(b) The superscript ^{2} indicates that this value, (O - E), is to be squared.

126. In χ^2 problems we will have different numbers of terms depending on the number of possible results. One number less than the number of possible results is called the number of degrees of freedom. For example, in matings of guinea pigs heterozygous for black coat color (i.e., carrying the recessive gene for white), the number of possible results are two: black and white. Those guinea pigs which are not black will be white. Therefore, the number of degrees of freedom here is _____ .

One.

Problem I (Use this problem for answering Frames 127-132.)

A coin is tossed 100 times and it is observed that 60 times it lands as heads and 40 times as tails.

---

127. From the 100 tosses we would expect:

(a)_____ heads and

(b)_____ tails.

This is a 1 : 1 ratio.

We know from previous work that we can expect heads ½ of the time and tails ½ of the time. From 100 tosses this would be:

(a) 50 heads.

(b) 50 tails.

This is an expected ratio of 1 : 1.

128. In setting up the χ^2 test, we will use the observed number of heads minus the expected number of heads in calculating the first term. Likewise, the observed number of tails minus the expected number of tails is used in calculating the second term.

Now, substitute the values given in Problem I and Frame 127 into the equations below:

(a) For the first term:
$$\frac{(\text{observed no. of heads - expected no. of heads})^2}{\text{expected no. of heads}} = \frac{(\quad\quad)^2}{(\quad\quad)}$$

(b) For the second term:
$$\frac{(\text{observed no. of tails - expected no. of tails})^2}{\text{expected no. of tails}} = \frac{(\quad\quad)^2}{(\quad\quad)}$$

(a) For the first term: $$\frac{(60 - 50)^2}{50}$$

(b) For the second term: $$\frac{(40 - 50)^2}{50}$$

129. We can now substitute these data into the χ^2 equation. For this problem:

$$\chi^2 = \Sigma \frac{(O - E)^2}{E} = \text{first term} + \text{second term}.$$

$$\chi^2 = \underline{\hspace{1.5cm}} + \underline{\hspace{1.5cm}}$$

$$\chi^2 = \frac{(60 - 50)^2}{50} + \frac{(40 - 50)^2}{50}$$

130. Now, using the answer to Frame 129, complete the calculation of χ^2. (In calculating χ^2 values, carry your calculations to three decimal places.) $\chi^2 = \underline{\hspace{2cm}}$

$$\chi^2 = \Sigma \frac{(O - E)^2}{E} = \frac{(60 - 50)^2}{50} + \frac{(40 - 50)^2}{50} =$$

$$\frac{(10)^2}{50} + \frac{(-10)^2}{50} =$$

$$\frac{100}{50} + \frac{100}{50} =$$

$$\chi^2 = \qquad 2 \quad + \quad 2 \quad = \quad 4$$

131. How many degrees of freedom do you have in interpreting the X^2 for this problem?_____

Note, there are two terms in the X^2 calculation since there are two possible results, heads or tails. Therefore, there is one degree of freedom (i.e., one less than the number of possible results).

132. When working chi-square problems, we will employ a table found in the Appendix, to determine whether the calculated chi-square value is sufficiently small for the deviations to be attributed to chance alone. Now turn to page 86 and read the directions for using the Table of Chi-Square Values.

Using the X^2 value of 4 (which you calculated in Frame 130) and remembering that for this problem there is one degree of freedom (Frame 131), locate the number 1 in the degrees of freedom (N) column. Go across from the N = 1 until you come to 3.841 and 5.412. Our calculated X^2 value of 4 lies between these two values.

The value, 4, is greater than 3.841, the value above which chi-square becomes statistically significant (at the 5% level) when there are 2 terms (or one degree of freedom). Therefore, it is likely that some factor other than chance was operating in this case.

In other words, the probability is that our observed deviations are.
    (a) too (large/small)_____ and
    (b) (may/may not)_____ be attributed to chance alone.

(a) large
(b) may not

> *Problem II* (Use this problem for answering Frames 133-139.) A coin is tossed a total of 10 times, and 7 of these times it lands heads and 3 times, tails.

133. What is the expected ratio of heads to tails?_____

The expected ratio is $1:1$.

134. (a) What is the expected number of heads?_____
     (b) Tails?_____

For ten tosses, we would expect:
(a) 5 heads and
(b) 5 tails.

135. How many degrees of freedom are there in this problem?
_____

Again, there is one degree of freedom.

136. Calculate the χ^2 value for this problem. $\chi^2 =$_____

$$\chi^2 = \frac{(O - E)^2}{E} \qquad + \qquad \frac{(O - E)^2}{E}$$

$$= \frac{(7 - 5)^2}{5} \qquad + \qquad \frac{(3 - 5)^2}{5}$$

$$= \frac{(2)^2}{5} \qquad + \qquad \frac{(-2)^2}{5}$$

$$= \frac{4}{5} \qquad + \qquad \frac{4}{5}$$

$$\chi^2 = \frac{8}{5} = 1.6.$$

137. For this problem, what is the maximum value that we could have for χ^2 and continue to attribute the observed deviations to chance? (See Table of Chi-Square Values in the Appendix.)_____

The maximum value for χ^2 with one degree of freedom is **3.841**.

138. (a) On the basis of the calculations made in Frame 136 and your answer for Frame 137, are you now willing to accept the data (7 heads, 3 tails) as a satisfactory approximation of the predicted 1:1 ratio? Yes___No___
   (b) In addition, are the deviations of the observed from the expected sufficiently small that they may be attributed to chance alone? Yes___No___

(a) From the table in the Appendix we see that our calculated χ^2 value of 1.6 is considerably less than the maximum allowable value of 3.841, which is associated with the probability of 5% or 1 chance in 20. Therefore, we *are willing to accept* the data as a satisfactory approximation of the expected 1:1 ratio, i.e., Yes.

(b) Furthermore, we conclude that the deviations observed in this experiment *may be attributed to chance* alone; i.e., Yes.

139. We can use the χ^2 table in the Appendix to obtain a more precise. answer as to the probability that the deviations observed are attributable to chance alone. For example, we calculated χ^2 to be 1.6 in Problem II, above. We have noted that we have one degree of freedom in interpreting this χ^2.

Now, if we look on the 1-degree-of-freedom row in the χ^2 table, we find that our value of 1.6 lies between the values 1.074 and 1.642. These χ^2 values are found in the .30 and .20 probability columns, respectively. In fact, our value of 1.6 is very close to the value (1.642) in the .20 column. This means that the probability that the deviations observed in this problem are due to chance is approximately 20%. In other words, if this experiment were done repeatedly, we might expect to observe deviations as large or larger than the ones actually observed in approximately 20% of the trials.

Now, given a χ^2 value of 1.325 in a situation where we have 3 degrees of freedom,
  (a) what table values of χ^2 lie on either side of the given χ^2 value (1.325)?_____
  (b) What is the probability that the deviations (upon which this χ^2 value was calculated) are due to chance alone?

_____

(a) 1.005 and 1.424
(b) The probability that the deviations are due to chance alone is between 70 - 80%.

Problem III (Use this problem for answering Frames 140-143.) A garden pea seed is planted. It is heterozygous for the alleles concerning seed shape, round (*W*) versus wrinkled (*w*). This plant was self–pollinated and from it 26 round and 6 wrinkled seeds were obtained.

140. The expected number of round and wrinkled seeds if these data were a deviation from a 3 : 1 ratio would be:

(a)_____ round and
(b)_____ wrinkled seeds.

The total number of seeds was 32. The expected results would be
(a) 24 round and
(b) 8 wrinkled seeds for 3 : 1 ratio.

141. How many degrees of freedom does one have in the inter-pretation of χ^2 in this problem?_____ _____

One degree of freedom.

142. Calculate χ^2 for these data. The χ^2 value = _____.

$$\chi^2 = \frac{(O - E)^2}{E} \qquad + \qquad \frac{(O - E)^2}{E}$$

$$= \frac{(26 - 24)^2}{24} \qquad + \qquad \frac{(6 - 8)^2}{8}$$

$$= \frac{(2)^2}{24} \qquad + \qquad \frac{(-2)^2}{8}$$

$$= \frac{4}{24} \qquad + \qquad \frac{4}{8}$$

$$= \frac{4}{24} \qquad + \qquad \frac{12}{24}$$

$$\chi^2 = \frac{16}{24} = 0.667$$

143. Look up this χ^2 value in the table and complete the following:
   (a) What table values of χ^2 lie on either side of the calculated value, 0.667?_____ and _____ .
   (b) What is the approximate probability that the observed deviations are due to chance alone?_____
   (c) Are you willing to accept the data as a satisfactory approximation of 3 : 1 ratio?   Yes____ No____

(a) 0.455 and 1.074
(b) The probability lies between 30 - 50%.
(c) Yes.

Problem IV (Use this problem for answering Frames 144-149.) In shorthorn cattle individuals heterozygous for the alleles *R* and *r* (which determine the coat color), are mated. The observed results of 200 calves from approximately 200 such matings were: 106 roan, 40 white, and 54 red calves.

---

144. From a cross such as this, what phenotypic ratio would one expect?_____

The expected ratio would be one red animal to two roan animals to one white animal or a 1 : 2 : 1 ratio.

---

145. How many red, roan, and white animals would be expected in the 200-calf sample?_____ Red; _____ Roan; _____ White.

From 200 animals, one would expect 50 red, 100 roan, and 50 white animals.

146. In this problem, how many degrees of freedom are there in interpreting χ^2?_____

There are 3 phenotypes (red, roan, and white) and there will be 3 terms in the χ^2 test; therefore, there are 2 degrees of freedom.

147. Calculate χ^2 for the data in this problem. $\chi^2 =$ _____

Using the χ^2 test:

$$\chi^2 = \frac{(O - E)^2}{E} + \frac{(O - E)^2}{E} + \frac{(O - E)^2}{E}$$

$$= \frac{(54 - 50)^2}{50} + \frac{(106 - 100)^2}{100} + \frac{(40 - 50)^2}{50}$$

$$= \frac{(4)^2}{50} + \frac{(6)^2}{100} + \frac{(-10)^2}{50}$$

$$= \frac{16}{50} + \frac{36}{100} + \frac{100}{50}$$

$$= \frac{32}{100} + \frac{36}{100} + \frac{200}{100}$$

$$\chi^2 = \frac{268}{100} = 2.68$$

148. In this problem, what is the maximum χ^2 value if the observed deviations are to be attributed to chance?_____

The maximum χ^2 value, with 2 degrees of freedom, is 5.991.

149. On the basis of the calculations made in Frame 147, and your answer for Frame 148, are you now willing to accept the data (40 white, 106 roan, 54 red) as a satisfactory approximation of the predicted 1:2:1 ratio? Yes_____No_____.

The probability that the deviations observed are due to chance alone is between 20 - 30% since our calculated χ^2 of 2.68 lies between 2.408 (30% column) and 3.219 (20% column). Therefore, Yes.

> *Problem V* (Use this problem for answering Frames 150-154.) Two pea plants, each heterozygous for color of seeds and texture of seeds, are crossed. We expect to get a phenotypic ratio of 9 yellow-round seeds to 3 yellow-wrinkled to 3 green-round to 1 green-wrinkled (i.e., 9:3:3:1 ratio). From a cross like the one described above 336 seeds were collected. There were 189 yellow-round, 50 yellow-wrinkled, 69 green-round, and 28 green-wrinkled.

150. Using the $9/16$, $3/16$, $3/16$, $1/16$ probability distribution, calculate the expected numbers of each type of seed.
  (a)_____ yellow-round;
  (b)_____ yellow-wrinkled;
  (c)_____ green-round;
  (d)_____ green-wrinkled.

The expected numbers of each type of seed are as follows:
(a) $9/16$ of 336 seeds = 189 yellow-round;
(b) $3/16$ of 336 seeds = 63 yellow-wrinkled;
(c) $3/16$ of 336 seeds = 63 green-round;
(d) $1/16$ of 336 seeds = 21 green-wrinkled.

151. How many degrees of freedom do you have in interpreting the χ^2 for this problem?_____

We have 3 degrees of freedom.

152. Calculate χ^2 for the data in this problem. $\chi^2 =$ _____

Using the χ^2 test:

$$\chi^2 = \Sigma \frac{(O - E)^2}{E}$$

$$= \frac{(189 - 189)^2}{189} + \frac{(50 - 63)^2}{63} + \frac{(69 - 63)^2}{63} + \frac{(28 - 21)^2}{21}$$

$$= \frac{(0)^2}{189} + \frac{(-13)^2}{63} + \frac{(6)^2}{63} + \frac{(7)^2}{21}$$

$$= 0 + \frac{169}{63} + \frac{36}{63} + \frac{49}{21}$$

$$= 0 + \frac{169}{63} + \frac{36}{63} + \frac{147}{63}$$

$$\chi^2 = \frac{352}{63} = 5.587.$$

153. In this problem, what is the maximum χ^2 value if the observed deviations are to be attributed to chance?_____

The maximum χ^2 value, with 3 degrees of freedom, is 7.816.

154. On the basis of the calculation made in Frame 152 and your answer for Frame 153, are you now willing to accept the data (189 yellow-round, 50 yellow-wrinkled, 69 green-round, 28 green-wrinkled) as a satisfactory approximation of the predicted 9:3:3:1 ratio? Yes_____No_____.

The probability that the deviations observed are due to chance alone is between 10 - 20% since our calculated χ^2 of 5.587 lies between 4.642 (20% column) and 6.251 (10% column). Therefore, Yes.

Progress Quiz—The Chi Square Test

The answers to these quiz questions are provided in the Teacher's Manual.

155. When and why is the chi-square test used?

156. (a) Write the equation for χ^2 =_____
 (b) the Greek letter sigma (Σ) means _____
 (c) the "O" stands for the_____
 (d) the "E" stands for the _____
 (e) the superscript, 2, means_____

157. In a family of 6 children, would 5 girls and 1 boy be a reasonable approximation of the expected ratio?_____

158. Remember that albinism in man is due to a recessive gene. If a couple, both heterozygous for this particular gene, had 8 children, we would expect the following phenotypic results:
   (a)_____ normal and _____ albino children.
   (b) This would represent a _____ ratio.

159. From a situation similar to the one described in Frame 158, would 4 normal children and 4 albino children constitute a reasonable approximation of the expected results?_____

160. If a pure black Andalusian chicken is crossed with a splashed white Andalusian (white with black splashes), the resulting offspring are "blue." If two of these "blue" individuals are mated, we expect 1 black: 2 blue: 1 white offspring. It appears that this occurs in much the same way as the red, roan, and white coat colors in shorthorn cattle. If "blue" chickens are mated and among 600 offspring, we observe 180 black, 190 white, and 230 "blue" chickens, would we be justified in attributing the observed deviations to chance alone?_____

161. If two guinea pigs, each heterozygous for coat color, are mated, does 195 black and 85 white offspring approximate the ratio expected from such a cross?_____

Problem VI (Use for answering Frames 162-164.) Let *"A"* represent the gene for one trait and *"B"* represent the gene for a second trait. Two organisms, each heterozygous for traits A and B, are crossed. The following results were obtained: 384 $A\_B\_$, 123 A_bb, 130 $aaB\_$, and 35 $aabb$.

---

162. What is the expected ratio for these data?_____

163. Using the expected ratio from Frame 162, how many of each type of offspring would one expect?

(a)_____ $A\_B\_$

(b)_____ A_bb

(c)_____ $aaB\_$

(d)_____ $aabb$

164. Do the results observed approximate the expected ratio?_____

IV

Comprehensive Review

If you have difficulty with particular frames in this review, re-study the related frames indicated. You must be able to work the problems in this review if you are to pass the final examination over the entire program.

165: In a family consisting of 2 children:
  (a) how many possible combinations or orders of birth for boys and girls are there?_____
  (b) What are these possible combinations?_____

	(a) *First Child*		*Second Child*		*Total possible combinations of boys and girls*
	2 possibilities	x	2 possibilities	=	4
	(boy or girl)		(boy or girl)		

(b)		
	B	B
	B	G
	G	B
	G	G

If you missed this frame review frames 3-24.

166. In a small wooded lot there are 10 specimens of deciduous trees. Each of the 10 represents a different species. A botany student is instructed to obtain 3 specimens from this lot, each specimen representing a *different* species. How many possible combinations of three different species can be made from the 10 species growing in the lot?_____

He has 10 choices for his first specimen. Once he had selected his first specimen, he has only 9 different species from which to choose his second specimen. Likewise, once he has selected his second specimen, he has only 8 different species from which to choose the third specimen.

10 x 9 x 8 = 720 possible combinations.

If you missed this frame review frames 44-46 and 56.

167. A plant having the genotype *AaBb* is crossed with one having the same genotype (i.e., *AaBb*). How many possible combinations are there for the offspring of such a cross?_____

There are 4 gametic possibilities for each of the parent organisms: *AB, Ab, aB,* and *ab.* Therefore, 4 x 4 = 16 = the total number of combinations for the offspring.

	AB	Ab	aB	ab
AB	AABB	AAbB	aABB	aAbB
Ab	AABb	AAbb	aABb	aAbb
aB	AaBB	AabB	aaBB	aabB
ab	AaBb	Aabb	aaBb	aabb

However, note that not *all* of the possible combinations are different; there are, in fact 9 *different* possible genotypes. For example, *aAbB* is really the same genotype as *aABb* or *AabB* or *AaBb*.
If you missed this frame review frames 3-24.

168. In a family of 3 children:
    (a) What is the probability that a couple's first child will be a boy?_____
    (b) What is the probability that in a family of 3 children, all 3 will be boys?_____

(a) There are 2 possibilities, a boy or a girl. Therefore, the probability of the first child being a boy is 1 chance out of 2 possibilities or $\frac{1}{2}$.
(b) Here, the important thing to remember is that each child is a *separate* and *independent* event and the probability for a boy is $\frac{1}{2}$ each time. Therefore, the probability that all 3 children will be boys $= (\frac{1}{2})^3 = \frac{1}{2} \times \frac{1}{2} \times \frac{1}{2} = \frac{1}{8}$. (Also, there is an equal probability of having 3 girls.)
If you missed this frame review frames 25-43.

169. What is the probability that a couple's first child will be either a boy or a girl?_____

The probability of a boy + the probability of a girl $= \frac{1}{2} + \frac{1}{2} = 1$.
If you missed this frame review frames 49-57.

170. The probability of an albino being born to parents heterozygous for this trait is $\frac{1}{4}$. What is the probability of such parents having 3 albino girls?_____

Probability of an albino		Probability of a girl		Probability of an albino girl
1/4	x	1/2	=	1/8

Prob. of first child being an albino girl		Prob. of second child being an albino girl		Prob. of third child being an albino girl		Prob. of three albino girls
1/8	x	1/8	x	1/8	=	1/512

If you missed this frame review frames 25-43.

171. In a particular family, the probability of having a child with type AB blood is 1/4.

    (a) What is the probability of having a *son* with type AB blood?_____

    (b) What is the probability of having a son with any other blood type?_____

    (c) What is the probability of having a son and his having either type AB blood or any other type blood?_____

(a)
Probability of AB blood		Probability of a boy		Probability of a boy with AB blood
1/4	x	1/2	=	1/8

(b)
Probability of any other type blood		Probability of a boy		Probability of a boy with any other type blood
3/4	x	1/2	=	3/8

(c)
Probability of a boy with AB blood		Probability of a boy with any other type blood		Probability of a boy with either AB or any other blood type
1/8	+	3/8	=	4/8 or 1/2

If you missed this frame review frames 56-59.

80

172. Indicate what each part of the binomial $(a + b)^N$ means.

_____

"a" equals the probability of one event occurring.
"b" equals the probability of the alternative event occurring (note that $a + b = 1$).

N equals the total number of events being considered.

If you missed this frame review frame 80.

173. Expand the binomial $(a + b)^4$. The product obtained is:

_____

$(a + b)^4 = a^4 + 4a^3b + 6a^2b^2 + 4ab^3 + b^4$.
If you missed this frame review frames 80-87.

174. One of the terms from the expanded binomial $(a + b)^4$ is $6a^2b^2$. Indicate how each part of this term may be interpreted.

_____

$6a^2b^2$
"a" equals the probability of one event occurring; the exponent, 2, refers to the event occurring twice (for which "a" represents the probability).

"b" equals the probability of an alternative event occurring; the exponent, 2, refers to the event occurring twice (for which "b" represents the probability).

The coefficient "6" means there are 6 possible orders in which we can have the one event occurring twice and the alternative event occurring twice.

If you missed this frame review frames 90-96.

175. In a family consisting of 4 children, what is the probability of there being 3 girls and 1 boy, in any order?_____

Using binomial expansion, $(a + b)^4 = a^4 + 4a^3b + 6a^2b^2 + 4ab^3 + b^4$. The term we use to determine the probability of 3 girls and 1 boy in a family of 4 children is $4a^3b$. If we let "a" equal the probability of a girl $= \frac{1}{2}$ and "b" equal the probability of a boy $= \frac{1}{2}$, then we have $4a^3b = 4(\frac{1}{2})^3 \times (\frac{1}{2}) =$
$4 \times \frac{1}{2} \times \frac{1}{2} \times \frac{1}{2} \times \frac{1}{2} = 4(\frac{1}{2})^4 = \frac{4}{16} = \frac{1}{4} =$ the probability of a family of 4 children having 3 girls and 1 boy in any order.

If you missed this frame review frames 70-107.

176. In a particular family, the probability of having a child with type AB blood is $\frac{1}{4}$. If this family consists of 5 children, what is the probability of having 2 children with type AB blood and 3 children with either type A, B, or O blood?_____

Using binomial expansion, $(a + b)^5 =$
$a^5 + 5a^4b + 10a^3b^2 + 10a^2b^3 + 5ab^4 + b^5$. The term we use to determine the probability of 2 children with type AB blood and 3 children with either type A, B or O blood in a family of 5

children is $10a^2b^3$. If we let "a" equal the probability of type AB blood $= \frac{1}{4}$ and "b" equal the probability of either type A, B, or O blood $= \frac{3}{4}$, and we have 10 different orders in which we can have 2 children with type AB blood and 3 children with type A, B, or O blood, then we have

$10a^2b^3 = 10(\frac{1}{4})^2 \times (\frac{3}{4})^3$

$\qquad = 10 \times \frac{1}{4} \times \frac{1}{4} \times \frac{3}{4} \times \frac{3}{4} \times \frac{3}{4}$

$\qquad = 270/1024 = 135/512$ or about $1/3.79$

If you missed this frame review frames 70-107.

177. When do you use the χ^2 test?

_____

When you want to determine whether deviations of observed results from the expected results are due to chance alone or to some other factor (or comparable answer).
If you missed this frame review frame 123.

178. Write the equation used for the chi-square test. _____

_____

$$\chi^2 = \Sigma \frac{(O - E)^2}{E}$$

If you missed this frame review frames 123-125.

179. In the χ^2 equation, _____
    (a) sigma (Σ) means _____
    (b) the "O" means _____
    (c) the "E" means _____
    (d) and the superscript, 2, means _____

_____

(a) "Σ" means the sum of all values of $\dfrac{(O - E)^2}{E}$

(b) "O" means the observed results
(c) "E" means the expected results
(d) "2" means the value inside the parentheses is to be squared.
If you missed this frame review frames 123-125.

180. When the chi-square value obtained by using the formula is sufficiently small:
    (a) we say the deviations from expected results are due to

_____

However, if the calculated chi-square value is sufficiently high,
    (b) we say that chi-square becomes statistically significant, and
    it is likely that the deviations from expected results are due
    to _____

_____

(a) chance or chance alone;
(b) some factor other than chance.
If you missed this frame review frames 123-132 and Appendix.

181. (Use the Table of Chi-Square Values)
For one degree of freedom, χ^2 becomes statistically significant when the χ^2 value exceeds _____

_____

3.841.
If you missed this frame review frames 132, 137 and Appendix.

182. When the calculated χ^2 value $= 3.841$ (with one degree of freedom), the *probability* that the deviations are due to chance alone is _____

_____

5% or 5 chances out of 100 or 1 chance in 20.
If you missed this frame review frames 137-139 and Appendix.

183. Shorthorn cattle heterozygous for the alleles R and r are mated. The 1000 calves produced from approximately 1000 such matings included 540 roan, 250 red, and 210 white calves.
  (a) Calculate X^2 for the data in this problem. _____
  (b) Using your calculated X^2 value and the Table of Chi-Square Values, are the deviations from the expected results due to chance alone? _____

(a) $X^2 = \Sigma \dfrac{(O - E)^2}{E}$

$$= \dfrac{(O - E)^2}{E} + \dfrac{(O - E)^2}{E} + \dfrac{(O - E)^2}{E}$$

$$= \dfrac{(250\text{-}250)^2}{250} + \dfrac{(540\text{-}500)^2}{500} + \dfrac{(210\text{-}250)^2}{250}$$

$$= 0 + \dfrac{(40)^2}{500} + \dfrac{(-40)^2}{250}$$

$$= 0 + \dfrac{1600}{500} + \dfrac{1600}{250}$$

$$= 0 + \dfrac{1600}{500} + \dfrac{3200}{500}$$

$$= \dfrac{4800}{500} = 9.6$$

(b) No.
If you missed this frame review frames 123-154.

184. Using the Table of Chi-Square Values, what is the *probability* that the deviations observed in Frame 183 are due to chance alone?

_____

_____

The probability is less than 1% that such deviations are due to chance alone.

If you missed this frame review frames 123-154.

Appendix

HOW TO USE THE TABLE OF CHI-SQUARE VALUES:

1. Work the X^2 problem to determine what the X^2 value is. For example, let us use $X^2 = 0.159$.

2. Determine the number of degrees of freedom and find that number in the first column on the left. For example, let us use $N = 1$.

3. Go across from $N = 1$ until we come to 0.148. Our X^2 value, 0.159, lies between 0.148 and 0.455. Looking up to the top row for the probability values, we see the observed deviations would be expected between 50 - 70% of the time. Therefore, we say X^2 is *not* statistically "significant" and the deviations can be attributed to chance.

4. X^2 is arbitrarily considered to be statistically "significant" when P is *less* than 5%; i.e., when the probability that the deviations are due to chance alone is less than 1 chance in 20. When P is less than 5%, we conclude that it is improbable that the deviations are due to chance alone. A probability (P) value of less than 1% is regarded as "highly significant" and we conclude that it is highly improbable that the deviations are due to chance alone.

TABLE OF CHI-SQUARE VALUES: (Abridged from Table III of Fisher and Yates: *Statistical Tables for Biological, Agricultural and Medical Research*, published by Oliver and Boyd, Ltd. Edinburgh, and by permission of the authors and publishers.)

n	P / .99	.98	.95	.90	.80	.70	.50	.30	.20	.10	.05	.02	.01
1	.000157	.000628	.00393	.0158	.0642	.148	.455	1.074	1.642	2.706	3.841	5.412	6.635
2	.0201	.0404	.103	.211	.446	.713	1.386	2.408	3.219	4.605	5.991	7.824	9.210
3	.115	.185	.352	.584	1.005	1.424	2.366	3.665	4.642	6.251	7.816	9.837	11.345
4	.297	.429	.711	1.064	1.649	2.195	3.357	4.878	5.989	7.779	9.488	11.668	13.277
5	.554	.752	1.145	1.610	2.343	3.000	4.351	6.064	7.289	9.236	11.070	13.388	15.086
6	.872	1.134	1.635	2.204	3.070	3.828	5.348	7.231	8.558	10.645	12.592	15.033	16.812
7	1.239	1.564	2.167	2.833	3.822	4.671	6.346	8.383	9.803	12.017	14.067	16.622	18.475
8	1.646	2.032	2.733	3.490	4.594	5.527	7.344	9.524	11.030	13.362	15.507	18.168	20.090
9	2.088	2.532	3.325	4.168	5.380	6.393	8.343	10.656	12.242	14.684	16.919	19.679	21.666
10	2.558	3.059	3.940	4.865	6.179	7.267	9.342	11.781	13.442	15.987	18.307	21.161	23.209

Key for symbols used in this table:

n = the number of degrees of freedom, 1 through 10 in the first column.

P = the probability of the deviations being due to chance alone; these values are in the top row. P can be read as a percentage by moving the decimal two places to the right.

X^2 values = all of the other columns of numbers.

Bibliography

The references given below may serve as sources of supplemental reading for interested students taking this program.

Bliss, C. I. 1967. *Statistics in Biology — Statistical Methods for Research in the Natural Sciences* Vol. I. McGraw-Hill Book Company, New York, New York.

Gardner, Eldon J. 1968. *Principles of Genetics.* John Wiley and Sons, Inc., New York, New York.

Hume, Beryl. 1966. *An Introduction to Probability and Statistics.* University of Western Australia Press, Nedlands, Western Australia.

Lerner, I. Michael. 1968. *Heredity Evolution and Society.* W. H. Freeman and Company, San Francisco, California.

Levine, Louis. 1969. *Biology of the Gene.* The C. V. Mosby Company, Saint Louis, Missouri.

Mode, Elmer B. 1966. *Elements of Probability and Statistics.* Prentice-Hall, Inc., Englewood Cliffs, New Jersey.

Mosimann, James E. 1968. *Elementary Probability for the Biological Sciences.* Appleton-Century-Crofts, New York, New York.

Srb, Adrian M., Ray D. Owen, and Robert S. Edgar. 1965. *General Genetics.* W. H. Freeman and Company, San Francisco, California.

Strickberger, Monroe W. 1968. *Genetics.* The Macmillan Company, New York, New York.

Winchester, A. M. 1966. *Genetics.* Houghton-Mifflin Company, Boston, Massachusetts.